EXAMPLES IN MATH
FOR KEY STAC

Other books by Ewart Smith available from Stanley Thornes:

Examples in Mathematics for GCSE Foundation Level
Examples in Mathematics for GCSE Intermediate Level
Examples in Mathematics for GCSE Higher Level
Examples in A-Level Core Mathematics
A New General Arithmetic
Easier Examples in Arithmetic

EXAMPLES IN MATHEMATICS

for

KEY STAGE 3

EWART SMITH

Stanley Thornes (Publishers) Ltd

First published in 1992 by:
Stanley Thornes (Publishers) Ltd
Old Station Drive
Leckhampton
CHELTENHAM GL53 0DN
England

0-7487-1390-5

A catalogue record for this book is available from the British Library.

Typeset by Tech-Set, Gateshead, Tyne & Wear.
Printed and bound in Great Britain at The Bath Press, Avon.

Contents

Preface

This book provides a plentiful supply of examples for practising, revising and testing the work for the National Curriculum at Key Stage 3. The book is divided into two parts. Part A contains fifty-five exercises with an emphasis on the fundamental arithmetic processes, puzzles and open-ended problems. Each exercise contains questions on several Attainment Targets and at different Levels. Part B contains forty topic-based exercises which range from Level 3 to Level 8. The code after each of these exercise headings indicates the Attainment Target(s) and Level(s) with which the questions are most closely associated. For example, 'Percentages (Ma2 L4, 6)' means that most of the questions in this exercise are based on topics found in Levels 4 and 6 of Attainment Target Ma2.

The work in each of the two parts of the book is progressive. The greater proportion of Part A can be attempted with little more than pencil and paper plus a modicum of basic computational knowledge. A calculator would be useful for this work but it is not essential. A supply of squared paper (5 mm) would also be an advantage for a limited number of questions. Each exercise is progressive, starting with some reasonably straight-forward questions, leading on to more challenging ones. There should be sufficient material to keep pupils of all abilities busy for most of the time – many less able pupils will find much in Part A to occupy them and may even surprise themselves with their contributions to the solutions of some of the investigational and puzzle-type questions. The exercises in Part B should be tackled when the particular topic has been studied thoroughly.

My thanks are due to Allan Snelgrove who checked the answers: to David Jenkins and the staff of Olchfa Comprehensive School, Swansea, for reading the script and to John Roberts who made several useful suggestions.

A separate answers booklet, which contains a matrix showing the Part B exercises in relation to National Curriculum Attainment Targets, is available.

Ewart Smith,
1992

Part A GENERAL EXERCISES

Exercise 1

① Write the following numbers in figures:
(a) forty-three
(b) seven hundred and eight
(c) five hundred and thirteen.

② Write the following numbers in words:
(a) 27   (b) 324   (c) 906   (d) 672.

③ In a third-year school election 83 pupils voted for Ramoud, 23 for Jane and 58 for Lee. How many pupils voted altogether?

④ Find the sum of all the odd numbers from 159 to 163 inclusive.

⑤ (a) What number must be added to 72 to give 164?
(b) What number must be subtracted from 936 to give 537?

⑥ There are 29 pupils in a class and there are three more girls than boys.
(a) How many boys are there?
(b) How many girls are there?

⑦ Copy the following sets of numbers. Put $+ - \times$ or $\div$ in each space so that the calculations are correct.
(a) $9 \square 4 = 5$ (e) $5 \square 4 \square 6 = 3$
(b) $7 \square 3 = 21$ (f) $8 \square 3 \square 4 = 1$
(c) $28 \square 4 = 7$ (g) $3 \square 4 \square 2 = 9$
(d) $8 \square 2 = 4$ (h) $2 \square 1 \square 3 = 6$

⑧ There are 12 sweets in each packet of a certain kind of sweet.
(a) How many sweets are there in 6 packets?
(b) Libby had 60 sweets from the packets she bought. How many packets did she buy?

⑨ Give the following numbers to the nearest 10:
(a) 57   (b) 82   (c) 26   (d) 44.

⑩ What time is it:
(a) 30 minutes after 4.48 a.m.
(b) 45 minutes after 11.45 p.m.
(c) 10 minutes before 1 p.m.
(d) 17 minutes before 10 a.m.?

(11) Copy these number patterns and fill in the blanks. The last term will enable you to check that your pattern is correct.

(a) 1, 3, 5,　,　, 13　　　　　(d) 5, 9, 13,　,　, 25
(b) 2, 6, 10, 14,　,　, 26　　(e) 3, 6, 12,　,　, 96
(c) 1, 2, 4, 8,　,　, 64　　　(f) 4, 9, 14, 19,　,　, 34

(12)

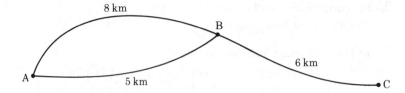

(a) How far is it from A to C:
　　(i) using the shorter route　　(ii) using the longer route?
(b) How many different routes are there from C to A?

Exercise 2

(1) What is the meaning of the 6 in each of the following numbers:

(a) 26　　　　(b) 62　　　　(c) 637　　　　(d) 6214?

(2)

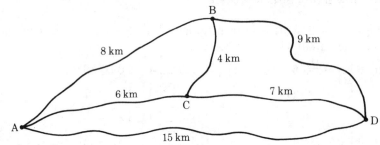

How far is it:

(a) from A to D via B
(b) from A to D via C
(c) from A to D by the most direct route
(d) from A to D via C and B?

(3) Motorway exits along a section of the M4 are numbered 5 to 27. How many exits are there in this section?

(4) Copy the following sets of numbers. Put + − × or ÷ in each space so that the calculations are correct.

(a) 7 ☐ 5 ☐ 9 = 3

(b) 8 ☐ 2 ☐ 6 ☐ 3 = 7

(c) 2 ☐ 9 ☐ 7 ☐ 5 = 9

5   (a) Sonia bought 8 cakes at 23 p each. How much did she spend?
    (b) Selwyn spent £1.61 on the same kind of cake. How many cakes did Selwyn buy?

6   Which is the higher score at darts and by how much, a treble 11 or a double 18?

7   Which number is 446 nearer to, 400 or 500?

8   (a) Write down the number that is half of a thousand.
    (b) Write down the number that is one third of 66.

9   In a street the houses are numbered from 1 to 23.
    (a) How many houses have odd numbers?
    (b) How many houses have even numbers?

10   Write down all the pairs of numbers between 1 and 20 inclusive, whose difference is 8 (for example 11 and 19).

11   Solve this cross-number puzzle.

Across   **1.** 124 + 223
            3. 743 − 211

Down   **1.** Number of days in a normal year
           2. 123 + 234 + 345

12   A farmer calls his workmen together to discuss how he can erect three fences, each in a straight line, to divide a square field into enclosures. The first workman draws a sketch to show how to divide the field into four enclosures. It looks like this

1
2
3
4

The second workman thinks that he can divide the field into five enclosures, the third into six and the fourth into seven. Can you show how they did it?

Exercise 3

(1) Write the following numbers in figures:
(a) sixty-three
(b) two hundred and seventeen
(c) eight hundred and nine
(d) three thousand four hundred and eighty-one.

(2) Write the following numbers in words:
(a) 75   (b) 602   (c) 439   (d) 5172.

(3) Find the sum of all the even numbers between 61 and 71.

(4) Nine coaches are hired for an outing. Each coach holds 49 passengers. All the coaches are full. How many passengers are there altogether?

(5) At the beginning of the year the form tutor gave out 234 exercise books. Each pupil received 9 exercise books. How many pupils were there?

(6) Give the following numbers correct to the nearest 100:
(a) 523   (b) 762   (c) 850   (d) 448.

(7) Write down the next two numbers in each of these number patterns.
(a) 1, 3, 9, 27, . . .   (d) 1, 2, 4, 5, 7, 8, . . .
(b) 2, 3, 5, 8, 12, . . .   (e) 3, 9, 15, 21, . . .
(c) 8, 10, 13, 17, 22, . . .   (f) 2, 6, 18, 54, . . .

(8) Look at the numbers 2, 8, 7, 15, 24, 27. List the numbers that are:
(a) odd   (b) even   (c) prime   (d) multiples of 3.

(9) Mr Handyman bought a new front door with lots of small rectangular glass panes. A sketch of it is shown opposite. One of his first jobs was to paint it. How many corners did he have to paint where he had to be careful not to get paint on the glass?

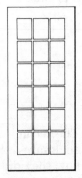

⑩

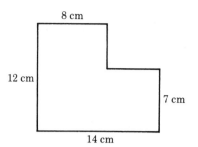

8 cm

12 cm

7 cm

14 cm

How far is it all the way round this shape?

⑪ To convert metres into centimetres we multiply by 100 since there are 100 centimetres in 1 metre.
(a) Convert each of the following distances into centimetres:
    (i) 5 m   (ii) 8 m   (iii) 35 m   (iv) $\frac{1}{2}$ m.
(b) How many metres are there in 3000 cm?

⑫

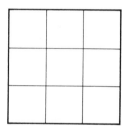

How many squares can you count in this diagram? (The answer is not 9!)

Exercise 4

① What is the meaning of the 3 in each of the following numbers:
    (a) 732   (b) 1309   (c) 3724   (d) 8321?

② Write, in words, the years: (a) 1945   (b) 1862.

③ Copy the following sets of numbers. Put + − × or ÷ in each space so that the calculation is correct.
    (a) 4 ☐ 2 ☐ 5 = 3
    (b) 8 ☐ 2 ☐ 3 ☐ 4 = 6
    (c) 7 ☐ 2 ☐ 3 ☐ 4 = 2

④

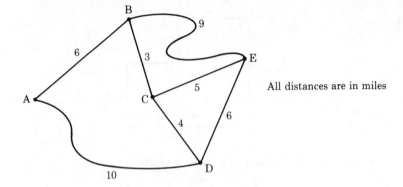

All distances are in miles

(a) How far is it from A to E by the shortest route?
(b) How far is it from A to E via B, C and D?
(c) Is it possible to travel from D to E, calling at each of the other places once only? If your answer is 'yes', in what order would you visit the other places?

⑤

Each disc shows three digits. Remove one digit from one disc and place it on another disc so that the sum of the digits on each of the three discs has the same total.

⑥ Today is Wednesday 8 October.
(a) What was the date:
    (i) last Sunday   (ii) a week yesterday?
(b) What will the date be:
    (i) next Saturday   (ii) a week tomorrow?

⑦ Solve this cross-number puzzle.

Across   **1.** 121×4
           3. 88×9
Down   **1.** $1000 - 573$
           2. $139 + 263$

8

(8) To convert centimetres to millimetres we multiply by 10, e.g.
8 cm = 80 mm.
Convert each of the following lengths into millimetres:
(a) 5 cm   (b) 20 cm   (c) 35 cm   (d) 74 cm.
How many centimetres are there in 400 mm?

(9) Eve left home at 7.35 a.m. and got to work at 8.53 a.m. How many minutes did it take her to get to work?

(10) How many bars of chocolate can Steve buy for £5 if each bar costs 52 p. How much change does Steve get?

(11)

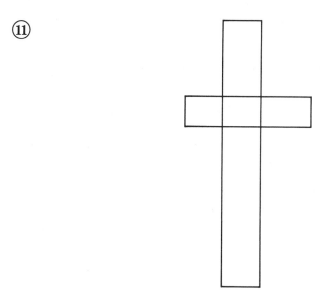

How many different rectangles can you see in this shape?

(12)

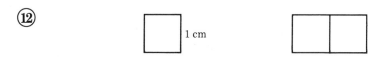

I have a lot of squares of side 1 cm. The perimeter of one square, i.e. the distance all the way round it, is 4 cm. When I put two squares together in a line to make a rectangle the perimeter of the rectangle is 6 cm.

(a) What is the perimeter when 5 of these squares are joined together in a line to make a rectangle?
(b) What is the perimeter when 20 of these squares are joined together in a line to make a rectangle?

1. Write the following numbers in figures:
   (a) six hundred and seventy-seven
   (b) seven hundred and five
   (c) four thousand one hundred and forty-two
   (d) eight thousand and seventeen.

2. Write the following numbers in words:
   (a) 549　　　(b) 302　　　(c) 8292　　　(d) 5047.

3. When a coach carrying 34 passengers arrives at the coach station, 13 passengers get off and 26 get on. How many passengers are there on the coach when it leaves the station?

4. What is the difference in the place value of the figure 5 in the numbers 542 and 157?

5. Find the sum of all the even numbers between 143 and 151.

6. Debbie visits the garden nursery to buy some strips of young plants. She spends £6.75 on nine strips. What is the price of one strip?

7. Round each of the following numbers *up* to the nearest 100:
   (a) 821　　　(b) 964　　　(c) 548　　　(d) 242.

8.
   •

   •　　　•

   Joyce plants three tomato plants to form an equilateral triangle. She has four more plants. How can she plant these so that the seven plants form six straight lines with exactly three plants in each line?

9. Copy and solve this cross-number puzzle.

   Across　1. 11 × 11
   　　　　　3. 21 × 15
   Down　1. 11 × 13
   　　　　　2. 15 × 11

(10)

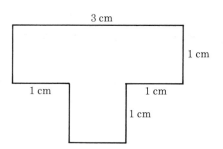

(a) Copy this diagram and fill in the missing lengths. What is the perimeter of this shape?

(b)

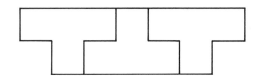

What is the perimeter when 3 of these T shapes are joined together in a line as shown?

(c) What is the perimeter when (i) 6   (ii) 25 of these T shapes are joined together in a line?

(11) Write down the numbers from 1 to 10 inclusive and then pair them off so that the sum of each pair gives the same total.

(12) Follow these instructions:

Step 1   Write down any three-figure number in which the number of hundreds differs by at least two from the number of units, e.g. 419 or 236 or 973 but *not* 707 or 514.

Step 2   Now write down the digits in reverse order, e.g. 419 becomes 914.

Step 3   Subtract the smaller number from the larger number, e.g. 914 − 419 = 495.

Step 4   Add this number to its reverse, i.e. add 495 to 594.

The result in this case is 1089.

Now try these four steps with any number of your own choice. Repeat the instructions six times for six different numbers, but do remember that the number of hundreds must differ by at least two from the number of units.

11

Exercise 6

(1) What is the meaning of the 8 in each of the following numbers:
(a) 8264   (b) 1087   (c) 6839   (d) 5008.

(2) In each of the following lists, put the numbers in order of size, starting with the smallest:
(a) 327, 372, 307
(b) 706, 766, 763
(c) 404, 1044, 44, 440
(d) 558, 508, 555, 505.

(3)

Two cards are shown with numbers on them. Each card has a different number on the back. The sum of the numbers on each card is seven. Write down all the possible two-figure numbers you can make using these cards.

(4)

Sunday	Monday	Tuesday	Wednesday	Thursday	Friday	Saturday
12 491	2493	4721	8492	10 215	9464	

The table shows the number of visitors to a zoo, each day except Saturday, one week last summer.
(a) How many visitors had there been that week up to and including Friday?
(b) The total for the week was 63 255. How many visitors were there on the Saturday?

(5) In a school with 310 pupils there are 10 more boys than girls. How many girls are there?

(6) There are 480 seats in a cinema. They are arranged in complete rows with 24 in a row. How many rows are there?

12

7 Yesterday was Tuesday 16 November.

(a) What day of the week is it tomorrow?
(b) What date will it be the day after tomorrow?
(c) What was the date last Friday?
(d) How many Tuesdays are there in this particular November? Write down their dates.

8 Write down the next two terms in each of these number patterns.

(a) 7, 8, 10, 13, 17, . . .
(b) 5, 10, 15, 20, . . .
(c) 5, 7, 10, 12, 15, . . .
(d) 1, 4, 9, 16, 25, . . .

9 Solve the following cross-number puzzle.

Across **1.** 63 − 21
          4. 245 + 171
          6. 500 − 365
          7. 201 − 128
Down   **2.** 97 + 146
          3. 222 − 136
          5. 78 + 79
          6. 54 + 106 − 141

10

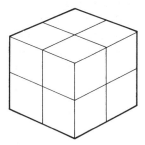

How many of the small cubes are needed to build the large cube?

11 A roll of fencing is 20 metres long. How many rolls of fencing does Wayne need to go around the edge of this square field?

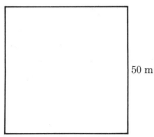

50 m

50 m

13

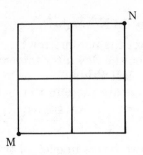

Malcolm and Naomi live on an estate. The road layout on this estate is shown above. Malcolm lives at one corner and Naomi lives at the other corner. Malcolm wants to walk from his home to Naomi's. He can walk only along the straight lines shown. He does not walk along any road twice.

(a) Investigate the different possible routes he can take. Draw them as shown in the two examples below.

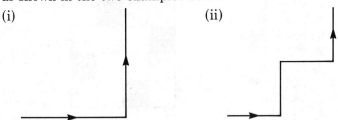

(b) Is there a shortest route? If your answer is 'yes', how many different shortest routes are there?

(c) Is there a longest route? How many different longest routes are there? Make sketches to illustrate your answer. (He cannot return to his starting point or pass through any point twice.)

Exercise 7

① Write the following numbers in figures:
(a) three thousand and sixty-five
(b) twenty-seven thousand three hundred and eighteen
(c) sixteen hundred and thirteen
(d) eight thousand and twelve

② Write the following numbers in words:
(a) 5269   (b) 7016   (c) 80 342   (d) 18 047.

③ At a general election 23 508 people voted for Kenton, 13 425 for Ibsen and 7264 for Morgan. If 3428 people failed to vote how many people were entitled to vote altogether?

④ Find the sum of all the odd numbers between 368 and 378.

⑤ Copy each of the following sets of numbers. Put $+ - \times$ or $\div$ in each space so that the calculations are correct.

(a) $12 \ \square \ 6 \ \square \ 4 \ = \ 8$

(b) $9 \ \square \ 3 \ \square \ 8 \ \square \ 4 \ = \ 1$

(c) $4 \ \square \ 3 \ \square \ 6 \ \square \ 8 \ \square \ 2 \ = \ 2$

⑥ Round each of the following numbers *down* to the nearest 100:

(a) 224   (b) 573   (c) 649   (d) 886.

⑦ We can write 60 as 2×30. Write down all the possible pairs of whole numbers you can think of that give 60 when they are multiplied together. (Try to do this in an orderly way.)

⑧ Show how you can pay 80 p for a magazine if you use:

(a) 3 coins   (b) 4 coins   (c) 5 coins.

⑨
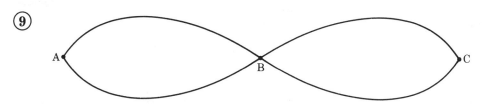

A, B and C represent three villages. There are two roads from A to B and two roads from B to C. How many different routes are there from A to C?

⑩ What is the smallest whole number that when divided by both 3 and 4 leaves a remainder of 2?

⑪ Solve this cross-number puzzle.

Across   **1.** 23×7
             3. 46×6
Down   **1.** 33×4
             2. 18×7

(12) The table shows the charges made by Worldwide Tours for holidays in Corfu. The prices are shown per person in pounds.

Date of departure	1 Jun –15 Jun	16 Jun –22 Jun	23 Jun –29 Jun	30 Jun –6 July	7 July –20 July	21 July –10 Aug	11 Aug –24 Aug	25 Aug –14 Sept	15 Sept –20 Sept	21 Sept –30 Sept
7 nights	249	269	289	299	305	319	315	309	305	269
14 nights	309	339	379	389	395	419	415	409	389	349

Child reductions: under 3 years – free
3–11 years – 30%
Single room supplement per week £55 per person

Use this information to answer the following questions.

(a) (i) Ms White intends going to Corfu on 26 June for two weeks and wishes to have a single room. How much will it cost her?
(ii) How much would she save by going two weeks earlier?
(b) A family of five, two adults and three children aged 10, 12 and 14, book a 7-night holiday departing on 15 August.
(i) How much will it cost?
(ii) How much extra would it cost them for an additional week?
(iii) How much would a 14-night holiday cost them if they left on 2 June?

Exercise 8 == **A**

(1)

Two cards are shown above with numbers on them. Each card has a number on the back and the sum of the two numbers on each card is 8. Write down all the possible two-figure numbers you can make using these cards.

(2) In a darts match Aziz threw: double 13, treble 6 and 16. What was his total score?

(3) Cheryl bought five oranges costing 14 p each and eight peaches costing 24 p each.
(a) How much did she pay for the oranges?
(b) How much did she pay for the peaches?
(c) How much did she spend altogether?
(d) She paid with a £10 note. How much change did she receive?

(4) Jim bought a 350 cm length of timber. He cut off two pieces, each of length 72 cm. What length of wood remained?

(5) Write down all the pairs of numbers between 10 and 30 inclusive whose difference is 9.

(6) What is the smallest whole number which, when divided by both 7 and 8, leaves a remainder of 3?

(7) Change the following amounts into pence:
(a) £3   (b) £12   (c) £5.60   (d) £9.35.

(8)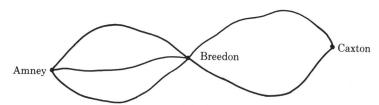

There are three roads from Amney to Breedon and two roads from Breedon to Caxton. Daisy wants to drive from Amney to Caxton via Breedon. How many different possible routes does she have?

(9) Can you arrange the digits 1, 2, 3, 4, 5, 6, 7, 8 and 9 in order, using each digit once, to make four numbers separated by either a + or − sign so that the answer is 100?

(10)

One afternoon, while Jason was looking in the mirror, he saw the reflection of a clock that was hanging on the wall behind him. What he could see is shown above. What time was it?

(11) Sonia makes up a pattern starting with 3 and 4. To get the next number in the pattern she adds the previous two numbers together. If the answer is more than 10 she writes down only the number of units. Her pattern is   3, 4, 7, 1, 8, 9, 7, . . .
Write down the next ten numbers in this pattern.
Does the pattern repeat itself?
If so, how many numbers are there before it starts to repeat?
Now start with 4 and 3 and see what happens. (You need to keep going for a long time!)

Use the timetable given below to answer the questions that follow.

ABBEY	1600	1615	1633	*1637*	1700	1716	1733	*1737*	1800	1831
BAGLEY	1603	1619	1636	1644	1703	1719	1736	1744	1803	1834
COWAN	1608	1623	1641	...	1708	1724	1741	...	1808	1839
DAWS HILL	1611	1626	1644	1651	1711	1727	1744	1751	1811	1842
EDEN	1613	1629	1647	1654	1713	1729	1747	1754	1813	1845
FARRAN	1618	1634a	1652	1700d	1718	1734	1752	1800a	1818	1850
GARR	1620	...	1655	...	1720	1736	1755	...	1820	1853
HOCKLEY	1624	...	1659	...	1724	1740	1759	...	1824	1857
INVER	1629	...	1704	...	1729	1746d	1804	...	1829	1903a
KILBRIN	1632	...	1707	...	1732	...	1807	...	1832	...
LEITH	1636	...	1711	...	1736	...	1811	...	1836	...
MACHEN	...	...	1714	...	...	...	1814	...	1839	...
NASH	1641	...	1717d	...	1741	...	1817a	...	1842	...
OAKFORD	1644	...	...	...	1744	...	...	...	1845	...
PENTRE	1647	...	...	...	1747	...	...	...	1848	...
QUARLEY	1652	...	...	...	1752	...	...	...	1853	...
REPPS	1655	...	...	...	1755	...	...	...	1856	...

ABBEY	1900	1931	2000	2031	2100	2134	2200	2231	2331
BAGLEY	1903	1934	2003	2034	2103	2137	2203	2234	2334
COWAN	1908	1939	2008	2039	2108	2142	2208	2239	2339
DAWS HILL	1911	1942	2011	2042	2111	2145	2211	2242	2342
EDEN	1913	1944	2013	2044	2113	2148	2213	2244	2344
FARRAN	1918	1949	2018	2049	2118	2153	2218	2249	2350d
GARR	1920	1951	2020	2051	2120	2156	2220	2251	...
HOCKLEY	1924	1955	2024	2055	2124	2200	2224	2255	...
INVER	1929	2001d	2029	2101d	2129	2205a	2229	2301d	...
KILBRIN	1932	...	2032	...	2132	...	2232	...	...
LEITH	1936	...	2036	...	2136	...	2236	...	...
MACHEN	1939	...	2039	...	2139	...	2239	...	...
NASH	1942	...	2042	...	2142	...	2242	...	...
OAKFORD	1945	...	2045	...	2145	...	2245	...	...
PENTRE	1948	...	2048	...	2148	...	2248	...	...
QUARLEY	1953	...	2053	...	2153	...	2253	...	...
REPPS	1956	...	2056	...	2156	...	2256	...	...

(a) How long does the 1700 from Abbey take to get to:
   (i) Hockley   (ii) Repps?
(b) At what time does the last train for Repps leave Abbey?
(c) Colin wants to get to Leith by 1815. What is the latest that he can leave Cowan?
(d) How many trains stop at Machen? What time does the fastest train for Machen leave Abbey?
(e) How long does the 2100 from Abbey take to travel from Farran to Pentre?
(f) Wendy arrives at Daws Hill station at 2033. She wants to go to Quarley. How long must she wait for a train? At what time should she get to Quarley?
(g) Sue gets to Cowan station at 1750. What is the earliest she can hope to arrive at Oakford?
(h) Havard arrives at Inver station at 6.24 p.m. What time should he arrive in Nash? Give your answer in a.m./p.m. time.

18

Exercise 9 ━━━━━━━━━━━━━━━━━━━━━━━━━━━

(1) (a) Change £5 into pence.
(b) Change 7 metres into centimetres.
(c) Change 40 centimetres into millimetres.
(d) Change 4 kilograms into grams.

(2) Copy the following sets of numbers. Put + − × or = in each space so that the calculations are correct.

(a) 8 ☐ 4 ☐ 7 ☐ 5

(b) 9 ☐ 2 ☐ 5 ☐ 2

(c) 2 ☐ 5 ☐ 3 ☐ 6

(d) 3 ☐ 4 ☐ 5 ☐ 7

(3) (a) What must be added to 293 to give 724?
(b) What number must be subtracted from 792 to give 637?

(4) Find the sum of all the numbers between 332 and 344 that are exactly divisible by 3.

(5) A box contains red pens and blue pens. Altogether there are 34 pens in the box. If there are 6 more red pens than blue pens, how many red pens are there?

(6) Phil wanted to know how many tiles had been used to roof his house. From one side he counted 15 rows with 24 tiles in each row. The roof on the other side of the house was identical. How many tiles had been used altogether?

(7) A school has four houses: Henry House, George House, Harold House and William House. In an inter-house competition each house plays all the other houses twice: once at soccer and once at hockey. How many games are played? Write out a possible fixture list.

(8) Can you complete this magic square so that the sum in any row, column or diagonal is 18?

(9) Paul has a one-metre length of metal that he must cut into four equal lengths. It takes him five minutes to cut off one piece. How long will his task take him?

(10) Solve this cross-number puzzle.

Across
1. $942 + 361$
4. $129 - 52$
7. $300 - 223$
10. $563 + 624$

Down
2. $107 - 73$
3. $223 - 186$
5. $525 - 446$
6. $29 + 28$
8. $18 + 53$
9. $756 - 658$

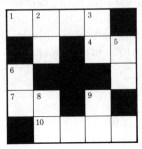

(11) Three discs are numbered 1, 2 and 3. They can be arranged so that the positive difference between the top two numbers is equal to the bottom number,

e.g.

(3) (2)   or   (3) (1)

(1)   (2)

When six discs are numbered 1 to 6 there are several possible ways of arranging them following the same rules.
One way is

(1) (6) (4)

(5) (2)

(3)

Can you find other ways of doing this? (You should find at least six.)

⑫
. . .
. . .

How many straight lines of different lengths can be drawn by joining any two of these six dots?

Exercise 10

① (a)

| 6 | 4 |

Two cards are shown with numbers on them. Each card has a different number on the back. The sum of the numbers on each card is 10. Write down all the different two-figure numbers you can make using these cards.
(b) Put the numbers you found in (a) in order of size, smallest first.

② Write down the next two numbers in each of the following patterns.
(a) 4, 12, 36, . . .
(b) 20, 18, 16, . . .
(c) 64, 32, 16, 8, . . .
(d) 50, 47, 44, 41, . . .

③ (a) Change 5700 centimetres into metres.
(b) Change 15 000 metres into kilometres.
(c) Change 21 kilograms into grams.

④ This year there are 1218 pupils in years 1 to 5 of Tetley Comprehensive School. If 273 fifth form pupils are due to leave and 217 new pupils are due to be admitted how many pupils should there be in years 1 to 5 of Tetley Comprehensive School next year?

⑤ A Cavalier King Charles spaniel has a litter of three bitches and two dogs. A year later each of the young bitches produces a litter of two bitches and two dogs. How many second generation puppies are there?

⑥ Tomorrow will be Saturday 15 June.

(a) What day of the week was it the day before yesterday?
(b) What was the date yesterday?
(c) What will be the date a week tomorrow?
(d) How many Saturdays are there in this particular June? Write down their dates.

⑦ In a school there is 1 teacher to every 18 pupils. There are 936 pupils. How many teachers are there?

⑧ The symbol > means 'is greater than' and the symbol < means 'is smaller than'. Hence 15 > 7 and 3 < 5.
Copy the pairs of numbers given below and place the correct symbol, either > or <, between them.

(a) 10   8
(b) 7   13
(c) 23   21

(d) 39   93
(e) 14   16
(f) 29   32

⑨

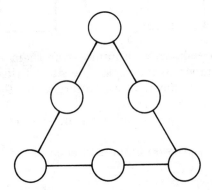

Copy this diagram. Using the numbers 1, 2, 3, 4, 5 and 6 once only write them one in each circle so that the sum of the numbers on each of the three sides of the triangle is 9.

⑩

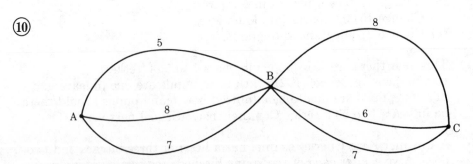

How many different routes are there from A to C via B?
List them in order of length, shortest first.

(11) Dave must take two 5 ml spoonfuls of medicine four times a day. The doctor prescribes a bottle holding 200 ml. How long will it last?

(12)

	4	5	6	7	
3					8
2					9
1					10

Mr Palfrey keeps budgerigars. He has 10 cages in a shed with one budgerigar in each and he always keeps the cage doors closed.
One evening his son Peter went into the shed and opened every second cage door – the first door he opened was the door of the second cage.
Later his daughter Jenny went into the shed. She opened every third door if it was closed or closed it if it was open.
When Mr Palfrey went into the shed the next morning how many cages did he find with open doors?
(Hint: set out clearly whether or not each door is open or closed after each child has left the shed.)

Exercise 11

(1) (a) How far is it all the way round a square field of side 50 metres?
(b) How far is it all the way round the edge of my kitchen door if the door is 2 metres high and 1 metre wide?

(2) The exchange rate for pounds sterling and German marks is:

£1 is equivalent to 3 marks.

(a) How many marks do I get for £55?
(b) How many pounds do I get for 1581 marks?

(3) What number do you put in the box so that:
(a) $\Box^2 = 49$ (b) $\Box^2 = 81$ (c) $6^2 = \Box$.

(4) A supporters club hires five coaches to go to a tournament. Each coach has 53 seats and all the seats are taken. How many supporters go to the tournament?

(5) There are 27 pupils in a class and there are twice as many girls as boys. How many girls are there?

(6) Frances has £1.90 and buys as many ballpoint pens as she can at 15 p each. How much does she have left?

(7) Stamps come in sheets of 200.
(a) What is the value of a sheet of 5 p stamps?
(b) What is the value of a sheet of 22 p stamps?

(8) Copy this pattern and fill in the blanks.

(9) Bryan leaves home at 8.35 a.m. to go to school. He returns at 4.10 p.m. How long is he away?

(10) (a)

How many different shapes can you make by joining these four squares together at their edges?

For example is allowed

but or is not.

(b) If a shape can be used to give a tiling pattern without any spaces in between, we say that the shape tessellates.
How many of the shapes you have drawn in part (a) tessellate?

24

(11) Solve this cross-number puzzle.

Across
1. $127 - 64$
3. $44 + 73 - 58$
4. 6×53
8. 330×41
11. $9 \times 10 - 9$
12. The first prime number greater than 40

Down
2. $3 \times 13 - 6$
3. $464 \div 8$
5. $625 \div 5$
6. 74×7
7. 9×89
9. $5 \times 8 - 27 \div 3$
10. $2 \times 19 - 4$

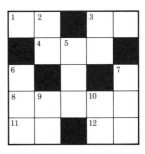

(12)

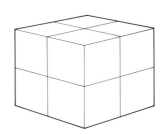

Eight white one-centimetre cubes are put together to form the two-centimetre cube shown in the drawing. The outside of this cube is painted red. How many of the small cubes:

(a) have two faces painted red
(b) have three faces painted red
(c) have four faces painted red?

Is it possible to put the small cubes together to give a white two-centimetre cube?

(13) A school proposes running a disco. The costs are:

disco and DJ £65
hire of hall £25
printing of tickets £7.50

(a) What is the total cost of running the disco?
(b) How many tickets must they sell at 50 p each to cover the costs?
(c) How much profit will there be if 450 tickets are sold?

In addition they decide to run a shop. They buy 300 cans of soft drinks at 18 p each and 250 packets of crisps at 12 p each. The drinks are sold at 22 p each and the crisps at 15 p each.

(d) How much profit do they make in the shop if everything is sold?

25

Exercise 12

(1) The five coins in Kay's purse have a total value of 60 p. What could the coins be?

(2)

$$31, 7, 21, 24, 13$$

Look at these numbers.
(a) Which of these numbers:
   (i) are odd numbers
   (ii) are prime numbers
   (iii) are multiples of 3?
(b) Write down all the factors of the largest of these numbers that is not prime.

(3) Bernie thinks of a number, doubles it and takes 11 away. The answer is 13. What number did Bernie think of?

(4)

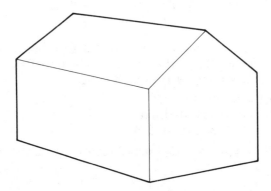

Tammy brought a model of a cottage home from holiday.
(a) How many faces does it have?
(b) How many edges does it have?

(5) My calculator has gone funny. When I press the $\boxed{+}$ button it multiplies and when I press the $\boxed{\times}$ button it adds.

(a) I press $\boxed{7}\ \boxed{+}\ \boxed{5}$. What answer do I get?
(b) My answer is 21 when I try to add two numbers. What should the answer be?

6 Elsie has some tennis balls and some bags to keep them in. If 9 balls are put into each bag, one ball is left over. If 11 balls are put into each bag, one bag is empty.
How many tennis balls and how many bags are there?

(Be logical! What if there's one bag? What if there are two bags? And so on.)

 7

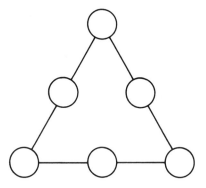

Copy this diagram.
Using the numbers 1 to 6 once only, can you write them, one in each box, so that the sum of the numbers on each of the three sides of the triangle is 12?

8 Rory buys a guitar for £50 and sells it for £60, buys it back for £70 and sells it again for £80. How much does he gain or lose in total on these transactions?

9

How many straight lines of different lengths can be drawn by joining any two of the nine points shown above?

10

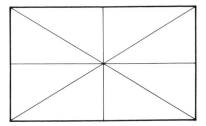

How many triangles can you see in this figure?

27

The dates of birth of three children are:

Linda 6/3/78
John 6/8/77
Francesca 6/6/78

(a) Who is the eldest and by how many months?
(b) Who is the youngest and by how many months?
(c) In which year will the youngest be 50?
(d) How old, in years and months, will the eldest be on 6 January in the year 2000?

⑫

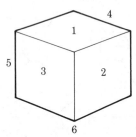

The numbers 1 to 6, or spots in place of the numbers, are put on the faces of a cube so that the sum of the numbers on opposite faces is 7. Sid wants to put the numbers 0, 1, 4, 5, 8 and 9 on the faces of a cube so that the sum of the numbers on opposite faces is always the same. How does he do this? What is the total on opposite faces?

Exercise 13

① (a) What is the difference in the value of the 6s in the number 6764?
(b) How many hundreds are there in sixty-four thousand?
(c) I think of a number, multiply it by 4 and subtract 40. The answer is 24. What number did I first think of?

② At a concert there are 57 married couples plus one child for every adult. How many people are attending the concert?

③ The distance all the way round a rectangle is 44 cm.

(a) The length is 8 cm more than the width. Use trial and improvement methods to find the length and width of this rectangle.
(b) Can the problem still be solved if the difference between the length and width is 12 cm?

④ If I reverse the digits in my age I get my son's age. Eleven years ago I was ten times as old as my son. How old is my son now?

⑤ Try drawing each of these shapes without lifting your pencil off the paper and without going over any line twice.

(a)   (b)

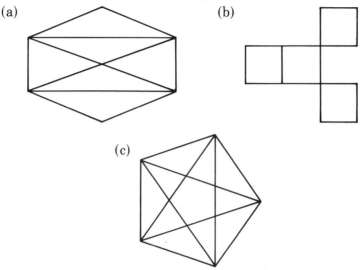

(c)

⑥ What is the smallest whole number which when divided by 3, 4 and 5 leaves a remainder of 2?

⑦ (a) How many complete turns does the minute hand of a clock make in 24 hours?
   (b) Where is the minute hand pointing at half past eight?
   (c) Where is the hour hand pointing at half past two?

⑧ Last Christmas Mrs Garnet bought every pupil in her class a bar of chocolate. For these she paid £8.41. How many pupils were there in her class?

⑨

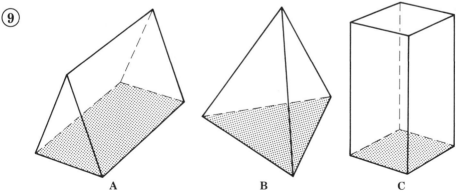

A   B   C

Name each of these solids. (In each case the base is shaded.)

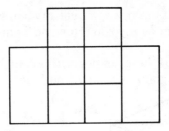

How many different squares can you find in this figure?

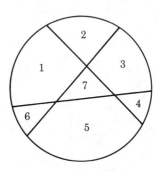

(a) Draw a circle (about 5 cm radius will do) and draw any chord. This chord divides the circle into two regions. Draw another chord to cut the first chord. Your circle is now divided into four regions. If you draw a third chord to cut the other two chords, but not passing through their point of intersection, the circle is divided into seven regions (see the diagram above).

(b) Draw a fourth chord that crosses the three you already have. How many regions are there now? (Note that only two chords cut at any one point.)

(c) Draw a fifth chord that crosses the previous four. How many regions do you have now?

(d) Copy and complete the table given below without drawing any more chords. You should see a pattern in the numbers in the second column.

Number of chords	Number of regions
1	2
2	4
3	7
4	
5	
6	
7	
8	
9	
10	

(12) In Stampdown the available postage stamps have values 1 p, 2 p, 8 p and 20 p. The full scale of charges for sending letters and packages by first class letter post is:

Weight not over	60 g	100 g	150 g	200 g	250 g	300 g	350 g
Charge in pence	20	30	37	45	54	62	71

(a) What is the maximum weight that can be sent by first class letter post?

(b) Copy and complete the following table which shows the minimum number of stamps, and their values, for the postage necessary to send certain letters and packages by first class letter post.

Weight	Postage	Minimum number of stamps	Individual values of stamps
45 g	20 p	1	20 p
80 g	30 p	3	20 p, 8 p, 2 p
121 g	37 p		
162 g			
245 g			
274 g			
333 g			

(c) Do all the packages heavier than 100 g need the same number of stamps?

(d) Which package, from the list given in the table, requires the greatest number of stamps?

Exercise 14

(1) Express each of the following amounts in the unit in brackets:

(a) $\frac{3}{4}$ of £2 (pence)

(b) $\frac{5}{6}$ of a year (months)

(c) $\frac{3}{10}$ of a metre (centimetres).

(2) (a) How many tenths must be added to 7.3 to make a total of 8?

(b) How many hundredths must be added to 3.48 to make a total of 4?

(c) How many tenths must be added to 17.8 to make a total of 20?

(3) A newspaper report stated that the attendance at an international match, correct to the nearest thousand, was 75 000.

(a) What is the largest number that could have attended?

(b) What is the smallest number that could have attended?

(c) What is the difference in your answers to parts (a) and (b)?

④ The Devon and Somerset Building Company send out bills on the fifth of the month to be paid by the second of the following month. Excluding the day on which the bill is sent, how many days are there in which to pay a bill sent out on:

(a) 5 September   (b) 5 October?

⑤ Form a number chain by using the following instructions.
Start with a two-figure number, multiply the tens digit by five and add to the units digit. Stop the chain when you get a single figure, e.g. $94 \to 49 \to 29 \to 19 \to 14 \to 9$.
Repeat this exercise using at leat six different numbers.

⑥ One number in each of these sequences is incorrect. Copy each sequence, replacing the incorrect number by the correct one. Write also the next three terms.

(a) 3, 6, 9, 11, 15, 18, . . .
(b) 1, 2, 4, 7, 12, 16, . . .
(c) 1, 2, 3, 8, 16, 32, . . .

⑦ Continue each of these patterns for two more stages.

(a) $1, 1 \times 2, 1 \times 2 \times 3, 1 \times 2 \times 3 \times 4, \ldots$
(b) $1 \times 2, 2 \times 3, 3 \times 4, \ldots$
(c) $1 \times 2, 3 \times 4, 4 \times 5, \ldots$

⑧

Jason has three discs. Each disc has one digit on each side and the sum of the digits on each disc is 13. All six digits are different. If Jason lays the three discs on the table to make a three-figure number:

(a) what is the largest number he can make
(b) what is the smallest number he can make?

⑨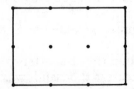

Mark 12 equally spaced dots as shown and draw a rectangle by joining the outside dots.

Join dots by straight lines to show how this rectangle can be divided into two identical pieces.
One possible way is

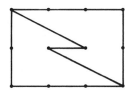

⑩ Rose and Stuart play a game with counters. To start, they have one black counter and one white counter, laid out on three squares as shown below.

The rules are that a counter can move, either to the adjacent square, if it is empty, or jump another counter if the square immediately beyond that counter is free. Black counters can move only to the right. White counters can move only to the left.
The object of the game is to get the black and white counters to change sides. The fewer moves needed the better.

(a) Rose goes first and her moves are

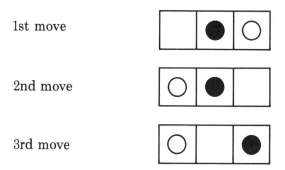

1st move

2nd move

3rd move

i.e. she completes the game in three moves.
(b) Stuart tries next and starts with one extra black counter and one extra square.

Can you suggest how he moves the counters to change sides but to keep the number of moves to a minimum?
(c) Now try yourself with two counters on each side.

⑪

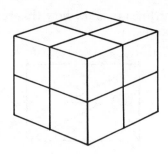

All the *edges* of a cube are painted black and there are black crosses on each face, as shown in the diagram. The cube is then placed on a table.

(a) How many vertical black lines are there?
(b) How many horizontal black lines are there?

⑫ Copy this pattern and fill in the blanks. The last term will help you to check your answer.

Exercise 15 ══════════════════ Ⓐ

① (a) I think of a number, take 5 away, and multiply the result by 9. My answer is 72. What number did I first think of?
   (b) What is the answer if you subtract sixty-six from six thousand six hundred and divide the result by 27?

② A cinema seats 650 people when full. There are 25 rows of seats, each row with the same number of seats.

   (a) How many seats are there in each row?
   (b) Seats cost £3 each and on one particular evening every seat is sold. What is the total income for the evening?

③ A recipe to provide enough cakes for six people includes the following ingredients:

   225 g butter
   375 g castor sugar
   3 eggs
   450 g flour

(a) Sara wants to make enough cakes for 12 people.
  (i) How many eggs does she need?
  (ii) How much flour does she need?
(b) Sam wants to make enough cakes for himself and Sally. Write out
    the quantities that he needs of the ingredients listed.

④ George has a wad of £20 notes that are numbered consecutively from
893 712 to 893 891. He is going to use these to buy a car. What is the
price of the car?

⑤ Using the coins in circulation, how many different ways are there to
make up each sum of money from 2 p to 10 p? For example 5 p can be
made up as:

  5 p, or 2 p + 2 p + 1 p or 2 p + 1 p + 1 p + 1 p
  or 1 p + 1 p + 1 p + 1 p + 1 p, i.e. in four different ways.

⑥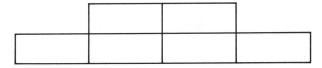

How many different rectangles can you see in this shape?

⑦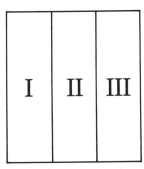

A dictionary in three volumes stands on a bookshelf. Each volume is
4 cm thick plus covers which are each 3 mm thick. A bookworm eats
its way from the first page of volume I to the last page of volume III.
How far is this?
(The answer is not 132 mm!)

⑧ Write each of the numbers from 100 to 130 as the sum of consecutive
numbers. Some of them can be written in several different ways,

  e.g. 111 = 56 + 57
  and 111 = 36 + 37 + 38
  and 111 = 16 + 17 + 18 + 19 + 20 + 21

(9)

(a) The train is due at 7.38. How many minutes are there before it should arrive?

(b) The bus is due at 21.08. How many minutes are there before it should arrive?

(10) A group of students from Mr Capstick's class went on a geology field course. Each recorded the number of fossils he or she found. The overall results are given below.

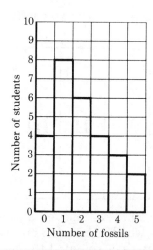

(a) What is the greatest number of fossils found by one student?

(b) How many students found exactly two fossils?

(c) How many students did not find any fossils?

(d) How many students were there altogether?

(e) How many fossils were found altogether?

(f) What was the mean (average) number of fossils found per student?

(11)

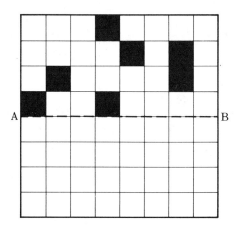

The diagram shows part of a cross-word puzzle.

(a) Shade the squares below AB so that the figure is symmetrical about AB.

(b) How many eight-letter words are there in this puzzle?

(12) Mike is making designs using squares of one centimetre side. The first four designs are shown below.

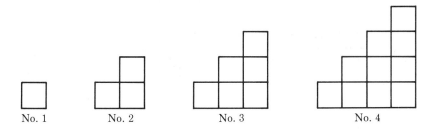

No. 1   No. 2   No. 3   No. 4

He counts the number of squares of all sizes that he can see in each design. In No. 3 he can see his first square with a 2 cm side. Draw the next four designs or figures in this pattern.

Copy and complete this table.

Design number	No. of 1 cm squares	No. of 2 cm squares	No. of 3 cm squares			Total number of squares
1	1					1
2	3					3
3	6	1				7
4	10	3				13
5						
6						
7						
8						

37

Exercise 16

① (a) Is 52 a multiple of 7?
  (b) Find the biggest factor of both 24 and 30.
  (c) Write down the next number after 24 that is prime.
  (d) Write 42 as the product of prime numbers.

② Find:
  (a) $\frac{1}{2}$ of 48   (c) $\frac{1}{4}$ of 64   (e) $\frac{3}{4}$ of 32
  (b) $\frac{1}{2}$ of 104   (d) $\frac{1}{4}$ of 16   (f) $\frac{3}{4}$ of 72.

③ What angle does the minute hand of a clock turn through when it goes from:
  (a) 12 to 6   (b) 6 to 9   (c) 9 to 12   (d) 4 to 8?

④ In the number 7.25 the value of the figure 2 is two tenths and the value of the figure 5 if five hundredths.
  (a) what is the value of the figure 3 in each of these numbers?
      (i) 31.49   (ii) 2.36   (iii) 5.13   (iv) 314.2
  (b) What is the value of the 7 in each of these numbers?
      (i) 20.07   (ii) 374.2   (iii) 7204   (iv) 5.147

⑤ What is the perimeter of each shape?

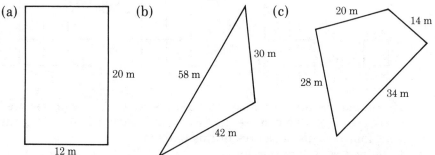

  (a) 12 m, 20 m
  (b) 58 m, 30 m, 42 m
  (c) 20 m, 14 m, 34 m, 28 m

⑥ Change each of these lengths into centimetres:
  (a) 17 m   (b) 3400 mm   (c) 9 m   (d) 420 mm.
  Which is the longest?

⑦ Use long division to find, to at least six decimal places, the decimal values of all the fractions from $\frac{1}{11}$ to $\frac{10}{11}$ that have 11 as the denominator.
  Are any of your answers recurring decimals?
  If so, how many digits are there in each cycle?
  Can you see any way of pairing your answers?

38

⑧ How many triangles are there in each of these figures?

(a)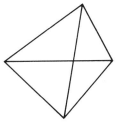

(b)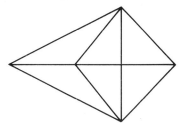

⑨ Complete each diagram so that the number in each square is the positive difference between the numbers in the two circles, one on each side of the square.

(a)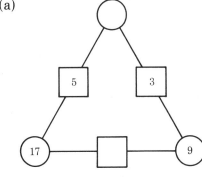

(b)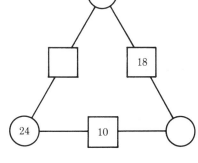

(c)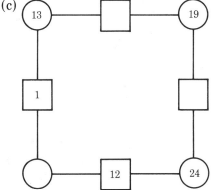

(d)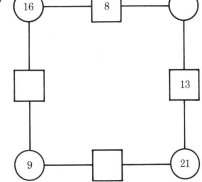

⑩ (a) Look at these chains of numbers.

$$29 \rightarrow 11 \rightarrow 2$$
$$57 \rightarrow 12 \rightarrow 3$$
$$95 \rightarrow 14 \rightarrow 5$$

Can you see what is happening?
Write down the corresponding chains starting with:
(i) 24　(ii) 79　(iii) 38　(iv) 99.

(b) Now look at these chains, which are connected with the chains in (a).

$$29 \rightarrow 40 \rightarrow 44 \rightarrow$$
$$57 \rightarrow 69 \rightarrow 84 \rightarrow$$
$$95 \rightarrow 109 \rightarrow 119 \rightarrow$$

Write the corresponding chains starting with:
(i) 24   (ii) 79   (iii) 52   (iv) 48.
(c) Look at this chain.

$$29 \rightarrow 40 \rightarrow 44$$

What number could come in front of 29?
(d) Make a similar chain starting with 94. What number could come in front of 94? What number could come in front of the number you have just written?

Exercise 17 ══════════════════════════

① (a) Which of these numbers is the smallest?

3.41, 0.27, 1.34, 0.72

(b) Which of these numbers is the largest?

5.17, 15.72, 2.73, 21.32

② The fraction $\frac{8}{12}$ can be simplified to $\frac{2}{3}$ since both 8 and 12 will divide exactly by 4. Simplify the fractions:

(a) $\frac{4}{10}$ (c) $\frac{4}{12}$ (e) $\frac{16}{20}$

(b) $\frac{5}{15}$ (d) $\frac{10}{15}$ (f) $\frac{20}{25}$

③

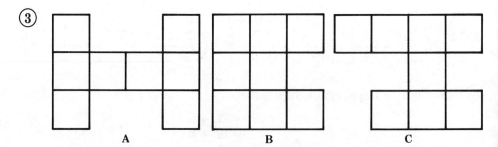

A   B   C

(a) How many squares like this [ ] are needed to cover each of these shapes completely?
(b) Which shape has the shortest perimeter?

④ Convert: (a) 5 metres into centimetres
(b) 3600 centimetres into metres
(c) 5000 metres into kilometres
(d) 1.5 kilometres into metres.

⑤ Fiona, Donna and Gert are three sisters. Fiona is 5 cm taller than Gert and Gert is 15 cm shorter than Donna. Donna is 150 cm tall. How tall is:

(a) Fiona   (b) Gert?

⑥ (a) Give: (i) 5297   (ii) 19 734, correct to the nearest hundred.
(b) Give: (i) 37 594   (ii) 8399, correct to the nearest thousand.

⑦ A frog dropped to the bottom of a well 5 m deep. It crawled up 3 m each day but unfortunately slipped back 2 m every night. How many days did it take to climb to the top?

⑧ Luke has some white cubes.

(a) How many faces does one cube have?

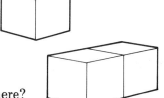

(b) Luke sticks two of his white cubes together and paints the outside of his solid red. He places the solid on the table.
  (i) How many exposed red faces are there?
  (ii) How many hidden white faces are there?

(c) Repeat part (b) for 3, 4, 5 and 6 cubes in a line. Make a table to show your results.

⑨ Study this month from a calendar and use it to answer the questions that follow.

Mon	Tues	Wed	Thurs	Fri	Sat	Sun
			1	2	3	4
5	6	7	8	9	10	11
12	13	14	15	16	17	18
19	20	21	22	23	24	25
26	27	28	29	30		

(a) Which month could this be, March, April or May?
(b) Tomorrow is the sixteenth of the month. What was the day and date a week yesterday?
(c) Today is the 13th. What day and date will it be a week tomorrow?
(d) What is the date of the third Thursday?
(e) The day before yesterday was the second Sunday of the month. What date will it be two weeks tomorrow?
(f) The day after tomorrow is the third Friday of the month. What is the date today?

41

(10) One morning Yanis and Sofie check their watches. Yanis' watch is 10 minutes slow and Sofie's watch is 5 minutes fast.

(a) At 09.55 what time is it:
    (i) on Yanis' watch
    (ii) on Sofie's watch?
(b) When it is 14.25 by Yanis' watch:
    (i) what is the correct time
    (ii) what is the time on Sofie's watch?
(c) When it is 16.45 by Sofie's watch
    (i) what is the correct time
    (ii) what is the time on Yanis's watch?
(d) Yanis and Sofie agree to meet under the market clock at 19.55. Sofie arrives on time by her watch but Yanis is 5 minutes late by his watch. Does Sofie have to wait for Yanis? If so, how long?
(e) Yanis wants to catch a train. He needs 8 minutes to walk to the station and gives himself 5 minutes to spare. The train is 7 minutes late. If Yanis assumes that his watch is correct, will he catch the train?

Exercise 18 ====================================

(1) A newspaper reported that there were 47 000 spectators at a match. Assuming that this was correct to the nearest 1000:

(a) what is the largest number that could have been present
(b) what is the smallest number that could have been present?

(2) Express the first quantity as a fraction of the second quantity:

(a) 40 p; 80 p   (c) 10 minutes; 30 minutes
(b) 50 p; £1   (d) 6 hours; 8 hours.

(3) Where does the minute hand of a clock stop if:

(a) it starts at 6 and turns through $\frac{1}{2}$ a revolution
(b) it starts at 8 and turns through $\frac{1}{4}$ of a revolution
(c) it starts at 9 and turns through $\frac{3}{4}$ of a revolution?

(4) What is the value of the figure 4 in each of the following numbers:

(a) 3.74   (b) 453.2   (c) 16.49   (d) 724.3?

(5) (a) Find 2 kg + 750 g and give the result in kilograms.
    (b) Find 7 m − 550 cm and give the result in centimetres.

(6) Find:
   (a) $15.92 + 26.08$ (c) $52.01 + 16.39$
   (b) $59.44 - 13.75$ (d) $80.43 - 58.77$

(7) Sometimes you do not have all the information you need to solve a problem. On other occasions you have too much information so you have to extract only that which is relevant.
Answer the following questions by making use of some of the additional information.

   (a) Allan is reading a book that has 120 pages. How many pages does he still have to read?
   Additional information:
      (i) each page has about 300 words
      (ii) he has read about two-thirds already
      (iii) he reads for about one hour every evening
      (iv) he reads about 20 pages an hour.
   (b) Nita takes 30 minutes to make a place mat. How many does she make in a week?
   Additional information:
      (i) each mat has an area of 400 cm^2
      (ii) she works for 8 hours each day
      (iii) her mats are packed in boxes of 6
      (iv) she does not work on a Saturday or a Sunday.
   (c) Sally, Terry and Colin made some cardboard boxes. They agreed to share what they earned equally. How much did each get?
   Additional information:
      (i) they made 250 boxes
      (ii) Terry worked 3 hours longer than Sally but 1 hour less than Colin
      (iii) each box cost 12 p to make
      (iv) the profit on each box was 6 p.

(8) (a) Write down any three-digit number, e.g. 834.
   Arrange the digits in order of size; once with the largest digit first and once with the smallest digit first, i.e. 843 and 348.
   Now find the positive difference between these two numbers,

   i.e. $843 - 348 = 495.$

   Repeat the process for your answer,

   i.e. $954 - 459 = 495.$

   These rules give us a chain of numbers. In this example we have

   $$834 \rightarrow 495 \rightarrow 495.$$

   (b) Form a similar chain for a three-figure number of your own choice. Try a few more. What do you notice?

43

⑨ Vicki thinks that her watch is 15 minutes slow when in fact it is 10 minutes fast. Relying on her watch she arrives at the station to catch the 12 noon train to London, allowing 5 minutes spare. Will she catch her train?

⑩ Complete each diagram so that the number in each square is the result of multiplying the two numbers in the circles on opposite sides of that square.

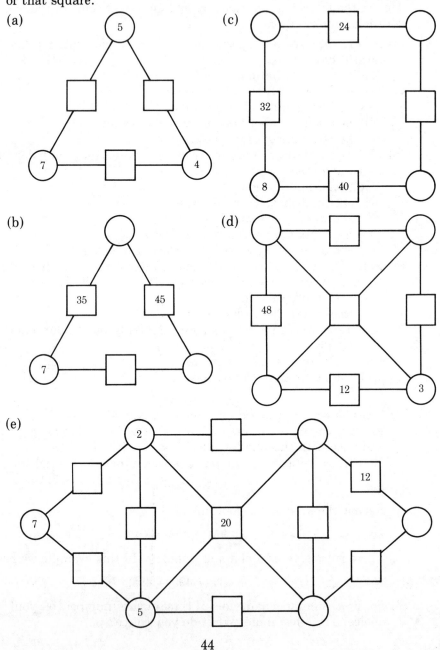

(a)

(b)

(c)

(d)

(e)

Exercise 19

① (a) If you stand facing north and turn clockwise through half a revolution, in which direction are you then facing?
(b) If you stand facing south-east and turn anticlockwise through quarter of a revolution, in which direction are you then facing?

② Write each set of numbers in order of size, with the smallest number first:

(a) 4.3, 3.4, 4.4, 3.3
(b) 7.9, 7.09, 9.7, 9.07.

③ Phil takes three parcels to the Post Office. Their weights are 840 g, 155 g and 2 kg. What is their combined weight:

(a) in grams   (b) in kilograms?

④ (a) Study these cuboids which have been made by putting several identical white cubes together. Write down the number of cubes needed to make each cuboid.

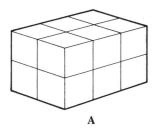

A

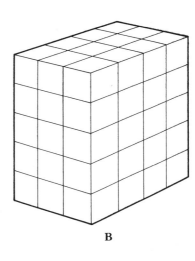

B

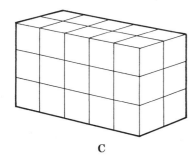

C

(b) The outside of each cuboid is now painted blue. For each solid write down:
  (i) the number of cubes with three faces painted blue
  (ii) the number of cubes with exactly two faces painted blue
  (iii) the number of cubes with no faces painted blue.

(5) Copy and complete this addition table:

+	4	7	11	23
3			14	
8				
13		20		
21				

(6) Nita bought some books from Postbooks plc.

(a) Copy and complete the order form:

Postbooks plc				
Book No.	Title	Qty	£	p
F 1030	*The Golden Hit*	2	16	90
C 7364	*Cooking for One*	1	9	95
R 4218	*Tangerine Dream*	1	8	50
F 2053	*The Plumber's Mate*	1		
	Order value		55	30
	Less 10% dis.			
	Sub-total			
	Add post & packing		1	95
Cash with order	Total cost			

(b) How much does one copy of *The Golden Hit* cost?

(c) How much would two copies of *The Plumber's Mate* cost?

(d) Unfortunately *Tangerine Dream* was out of stock. Make out an invoice for the goods Nita received. Don't forget to allow discount. How much of a refund should Nita get?

(7) Copy and complete each of the following statements:

(a) 10 boys out of 40 boys is ____ %

(b) 30 girls out of 60 girls is ____ %

(c) 150 adults out of 200 adults is ____ %.

(8) On a calculator Molly is allowed to use only the keys $\boxed{3}$ $\boxed{5}$ $\boxed{\times}$ $\boxed{-}$ $\boxed{=}$

To get 7 she can press

$\boxed{5}$ $\boxed{\times}$ $\boxed{5}$ $\boxed{-}$ $\boxed{3}$ $\boxed{-}$ $\boxed{3}$ $\boxed{-}$ $\boxed{3}$ $\boxed{-}$ $\boxed{3}$ $\boxed{-}$ $\boxed{3}$ $\boxed{=}$

To get 9 she can press

$\boxed{5}$ $\boxed{\times}$ $\boxed{3}$ $\boxed{-}$ $\boxed{3}$ $\boxed{-}$ $\boxed{3}$ $\boxed{=}$

What can she press to get:

(a) 2   (b) 6   (c) 10   (d) 22?

9 (a) Write the next 5 terms in the pattern

$$1, 5, 13, 25, 41, \ldots$$

(b) Complete this magic square so that the total of each column, row and diagonal is 21.

		6
7		
		4

10 (a) Beth has written three letters and addressed three envelopes. In how many different ways can she put all three letters in the wrong envelopes?
It will probably help you if you label the envelopes A, B and C, the letters that should go into these envelopes a, b and c, and construct a table to show the different possibilities for putting all the letters in the wrong envelopes.
The table below gives one solution to the problem.

	Envelopes		
	A	B	C
Letters	c	a	b

(b) Baldrick writes four letters and addresses four envelopes. In how many different ways can he put all four letters in the wrong envelopes? Use the idea that helped you to do part (a).

Exercise 20

1 Set A 15.2 5.02 2.52 21.4 2.05
  Set B 6.92 6.22 6.29 29.6 6.09

from each set of numbers write down:
(a) the largest number
(b) the smallest number
(c) the difference between the largest number and the smallest number.

2 How many posts are needed to erect 100 metres of fencing if one post is placed every 2 metres?

47

③

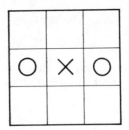

(a) How many squares are there in this figure?
(b) How many of these squares contain an ✕?
(c) How many of these squares contain an ○?

④ Nigel has eight sticks, four are each 10 cm long and four are each 5 cm long. How can he lay them on the table to enclose three squares all of the same size? There are to be no unusual projections.

⑤ (a) Give three multiples of 7.
(b) Write down the next three numbers after 30 that are prime.
(c) Is it true to say that 7 is a multiple of 21?
(d) Find the largest factor of both 18 and 24.

⑥

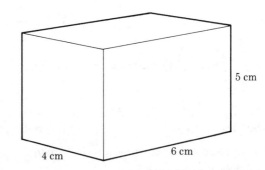

Wooden blocks measuring 1 cm × 1 cm × 1 cm are stored in a box measuring 6 cm × 4 cm × 5 cm. What is the largest number of such blocks that can be put in this box?

⑦ Andrew decides to take a ten-lesson course in guitar playing. The lessons are arranged to take place every fourth day starting on Friday 1 September. What is the day and date of his last lesson?

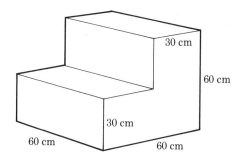

(8)

The sketch shows a solid piece of concrete that is to be used as steps.

(a) (i) How many faces, or flat areas, does this shape have?
    (ii) How many of these faces are rectangles?
(b) (i) How many edges does it have?
    (ii) How many of these edges are 60 cm long?
(c) How many corners does it have? Are all the corners of the same kind?

(9)

. . . .

. . . .

. . . .

How many straight lines of different lengths can be drawn by joining any two of the twelve dots shown above?

(10) At a committee meeting of the local cricket club, 5 voted in favour of building a new pavilion and 8 voted against. How many of the committee need to be persuaded to change their minds if the building of the new pavilion is to go ahead?

(11) Look at the following addition:

$$273$$
$$546 +$$
$$\overline{819}$$

Each digit from 1 to 9 is used once. Can you find other pairs of three-figure numbers which when added together give a third three-figure number such that every digit from 1 to 9 has been used once and once only?

(There are more than 30 different ways of doing this. If you can find 10 you are doing well.)

Exercise 21

① How many triangles can you see in this figure?

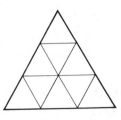

② (a) Is 32 a prime number?
  (b) The first prime number is 2. Find the sum of the first and fifth prime numbers? Is your answer a prime number?
  (c) Multiply the third prime number by the sixth prime number. Is your answer a prime number?

③ What value does each of these arrows point at?

(a)

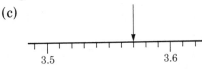

(c)

(b)

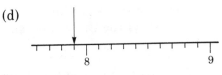

(d)

④ Dennis draws a symmetrical shape and folds it along the line of symmetry. When it is folded he shows it to Frieda, his sister. This is what Frieda sees:

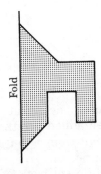

Draw Dennis' original shape.

(5) There are six players in a chess club competition. Each player is to play the other five once. Use the table to find out how many matches must be played. How many games do not involve Davis?

	Andrews	Box	Caton	Davis	Edge	Farley
Andrews						
Box						
Caton						
Davis						
Edge						
Farley						

(6) A motorist drives from London to Birmingham, a distance of 108 kilometres.
Find:
(a) the number of litres of petrol required for this journey if the car travels 12 kilometres on each litre of petrol
(b) the cost of the petrol at 40 p per litre
(c) the distance from London to Birmingham in miles, given that 8 kilometres is equal to 5 miles.

(7)

Cambridge				
£2.25	Dullingham			
£2.50	90 p	Newmarket		
£2.75	£2	£1.35	Kennett	
£4.10	£2.76	£2.44	£1.75	Bury St Edmunds

The table shows the single rail fares for adults on trains between Cambridge and Bury St Edmunds. Children travel at half the adult fare.
(a) How much would it cost for three adults to travel from Cambridge to Kennett?
(b) How much would it cost for four children to travel from Dullingham to Bury St Edmunds?
(c) What is the fare for two adults and three children for a return journey from Newmarket to Bury St Edmunds?

(8) A train leaves Manchester for London every hour on the hour and a train leaves London for Manchester every hour on the half hour. The journey takes two hours each way. Mrs Davenport leaves Manchester by train to go to London. How many trains travelling from London to Manchester pass her?

(9) Copy each of these magic squares. One line of numbers in each is complete. Find the total of the numbers in this line and fill in the blanks so that all the rows, columns and diagonals have the same total.

(a)

4	9		16
	7	11	
	6	10	3
	12		

(b)

	8	12	
3	10	9	
	11		
16	5		4

(c)

16			13
	11	10	8
		6	
4	14		1

(d)

11			2	9
10	12			
4		13	20	22
23	5		14	16
		1		15

(e)

	3	22	16	
	21		14	8
25	19	13	7	
18		6		24
	10	4		17

(10) (a) Write down any four-digit number, e.g. 7295.
   (i) Write down the positive difference between the first digit and the second digit, i.e. $7 - 2 = 5$.
   (ii) Repeat this for the 2nd and 3rd digits, i.e. $9 - 2 = 7$.
   (iii) Repeat this for the 3rd and 4th digits, i.e. $9 - 5 = 4$.
   (iv) Repeat this for the 4th and 1st digits, i.e. $7 - 5 = 2$.

(b) Use your answers to (a) to write down a new four-digit number, i.e. 5742.

(c) Keep on repeating what you have done until you cannot go any further.

(d) Start with any other 4-digit number and go through the whole process again. What do you notice? Try again with yet another number.

(11) The product of the ages of a mother and her three children is 4200. The son's age is equal to the sum of the ages of his two sisters.
(a) How old is the mother?
(b) How old is the elder sister?

52

Exercise 22 ══════════════════════════════════ Ⓐ

①　The perimeter of the L-shape shown below is 8 cm.

What is the perimeter when (a) 5 (b) 10 (c) 20, similar shapes are placed together in a line, e.g.

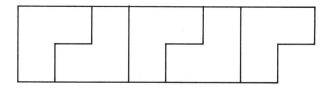

②　A 15-day tour of Spain costs £465. How much is this per day?

③　One morning while Betty was getting ready to go shopping she glanced in the mirror and saw the reflection of the kitchen clock. What she saw is shown below. Both hands of her clock are the same length. What time was it?

④　Write every number from 130 to 150 as the sum of consecutive integers,
e.g. 141 = 70 + 71
or　141 = 46 + 47 + 48
or　141 = 21 + 22 + 23 + 24 + 25 + 26.
Which number can be written in the greatest number of different ways?

(5) If a shape is drawn on a grid Pick's theorem tells us that if N is the number of points where the grid lines intersect on the boundary and I is the number of points where the grid lines intersect inside the boundary then the area, A, of the shape is given by the formula

$$A = \frac{N}{2} + I - 1 \text{ squares.}$$

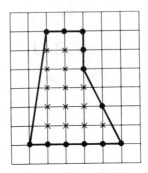

For example, for the shape drawn above,
$N = 12$ (marked with dots)
and $I = 14$ (marked with crosses)
so $A = \frac{12}{2} + 14 - 1$
$\quad\ = 19$ squares.

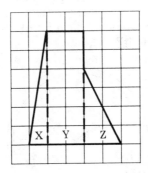

By dividing the shape into two triangles and a rectangle we can see that:

    area of X =   3 squares
    area of Y = 12 squares
    area of Z =   4 squares.

Hence the total area of the shape is 19 squares, which agrees with the result we got using Pick's theorem.
Use Pick's theorem to find the number of squares needed to cover each of the following shapes. Check your result using another method.

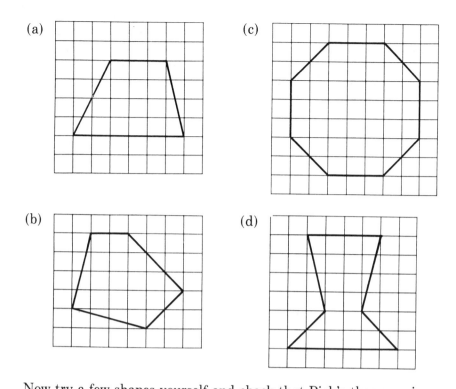

(a)   (c)

(b)   (d)

Now try a few shapes yourself and check that Pick's theorem gives the result you get using a different method.

6 How many small cubes are used to make each of these stacks?

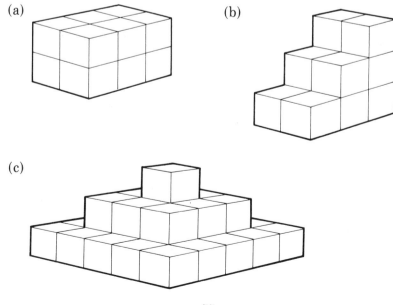

(a)   (b)

(c)

(7) Lois keeps all her best postage stamps in envelopes. If 11 stamps are put in each envelope, one stamp is left over, whereas if 15 are put in each envelope one envelope is empty. How many stamps and how many envelopes are there?

(8)

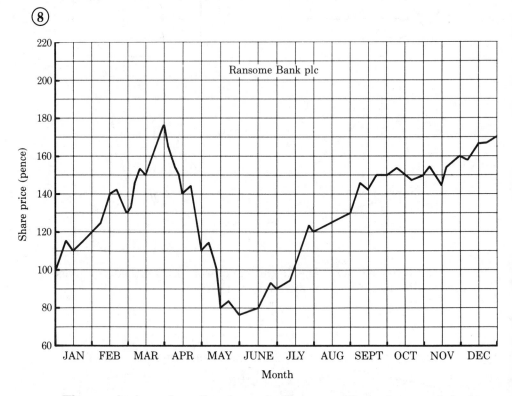

The graph shows how the shares in Ransome Bank plc moved during their first year of issue. The 25 p shares were issued at a price of 100 p each on 1 January.

(a) Use the graph to estimate:
   (i) the highest price during the first three months of the year
   (ii) the lowest price during the last three months of the year
   (iii) the date and value for the highest price for these shares
   (iv) the date and value for the lowest price for these shares.
(b) (i) When would have been the best time to buy these shares?
   (ii) when would have been the worst time to buy these shares?
(c) Would it have been possible to double your money by buying and selling these shares? Give reasons for your answer.

(9) In how many different ways can you choose six coins to give a total of 80 p? List them.

⑩ What speed is shown on each of these dials

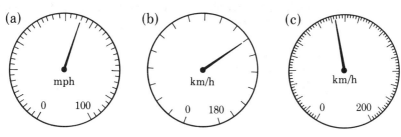

(a) mph 0 100

(b) km/h 0 180

(c) km/h 0 200

Exercise 23

① Anne and Joe have 55 records between them. Joe has three more records than Anne. How many records does each person have?

②

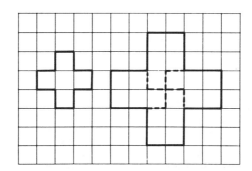

Draw these two Greek crosses on squared paper. Suppose that the large cross is cut into four identical pieces by cutting along the dotted lines. Show on squared paper how you would put the five pieces shown above together to form a square.

③ State whether or not each of the following statements is true or false:

(a) $\sqrt{9} + \sqrt{16} = \sqrt{25}$

(b) $\sqrt{25}$ is greater than $\sqrt{9} + \sqrt{16}$

(c) $\sqrt{9} + \sqrt{16}$ is smaller than $\sqrt{25}$.

④ Don, Gary and Dino are three brothers. Their average age is 11 years. Don is 3 years younger than Gary and Dino is 3 years older than Don. How old is each?

(5) Find all the whole numbers from 1 to 30 that can be made by adding two or more consecutive whole numbers. How many of these can be done in more than one way?

(6) Four different right-angled triangles can be drawn on a grid of nine dots. One of them is

Can you draw the other three?
Investigate the problem further using the grids of 16 and 25 dots given below.

(7) Imagine a clock face marked as shown below. Suppose that it has a single hand set on the 5. What if we move it round a further 3. Where does it finish? On the 1.
Using this kind of arithmetic

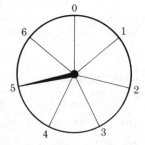

$$5 + 3 = 1$$
Similarly
$$4 + 6 = 3$$

Now try these

(a) $4 + 4 =$
(b) $5 + 4 =$

(c) $6 + 3 =$
(d) $2 + 6 =$

(e) $5 + 6 =$
(f) $4 + 6 =$

(g) $4 + 4 + 4 =$
(h) $4 + 5 + 6 =$

(i) $3 + 5 + 6 =$
(j) $5 + 2 + 5 =$

(k) $6 + 6 + 6 =$
(l) $5 + 4 + 5 + 4 =$

Now make up a clock face with the numbers 0 to 5 on it and work out these:

(m) 3 + 3 =   (p) 3 + 5 =   (r) 2 + 3 + 4 =
(n) 4 + 4 =   (q) 2 + 4 =   (s) 1 + 4 + 5 =

While this is just a game here it can have a value later.

⑧

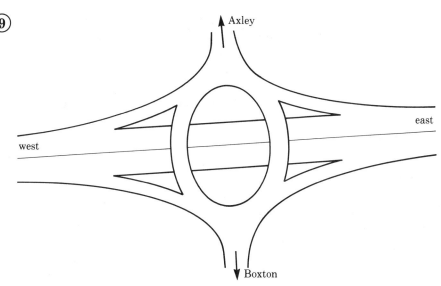

		First dice					
		1	2	3	4	5	6
	1						
	2		4				
Second	3				7		
dice	4						
	5						
	6			9			

This table can be used to find the total scores possible when two dice are rolled. When the 1st dice shows 2 and the 2nd dice shows 2 the score is 4. When the 1st dice shows 3 and the 2nd dice shows 6 the score is 9.

(a) Copy this table and complete it.
(b) Which scores are the hardest to get?
(c) Which scores are the easiest to get?

⑨

Axley

east

west

Boxton

The plan shows the road layout where the A46 crosses the M4 by means of a flyover. Sketch this layout.
On your sketch show:

(a) with a dotted line, the route taken by a lorry travelling from the east whose driver wishes to take the road to Axley.
(b) with a continuous line, the route taken by a coach from Boxton whose driver wants to go west on the M4.

(10) It is a strange fact that

$$12 \times 12 = 144 \text{ and } 21 \times 21 = 441,$$

i.e. the numbers in the first multiplication are reversed to give the numbers in the second multiplication, and both multiplications are correct.
Can you find any more numbers that have this property?

Exercise 24

(1) Ted has six coins that have a total value of 40 p. What values could these coins have? Is there more than one answer?

(2) A safe can be opened by the correct combination of three digits. When 418 is tried, one digit is wrong; when 238 is tried, one digit is wrong and when 437 is tried, one digit is still wrong. What is the correct combination?

(3) The marked price of a hi-fi system is £245. In a sale it is offered at '20% off the marked price'. Calculate the sale price of this hi-fi system.

(4) The digits 1 to 9, used once each, can be written as the fraction $\dfrac{13458}{6729}$ which simplifies to give 2.

Can you arrange the digits 1 to 9, using each digit just once, to give a fraction that simplifies to give: (a) 3   (b) 5?

(5) Jasper accepted a challenge to climb to the top of a fireman's pole that was 12 metres tall. He could climb at a rate of 1 metre per minute but slipped back 1 metre during every minute that he rested. He went from top to bottom by repeatedly climbing for three minutes, then resting for one minute. How long did it take him to climb to the top?

(6) A coach leaves Newport on the hour every hour to go to Bridgetown and a coach leaves Bridgetown to go to Newport on every hour and every half hour. The coach journey between the two towns takes $1\frac{1}{2}$ hours. How many coaches going from Bridgetown to Newport does Eli pass as she journeys from Newport to Bridgetown?

60

(7) Copy each of these diagrams and draw the reflection of each shape in the dotted line.

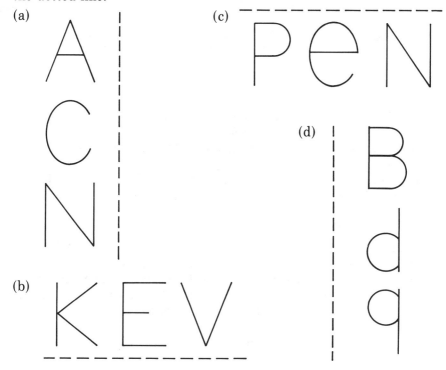

(a)

(b)

(c)

(d)

(8) In a closing down sale a retailer sold two pairs of shoes at £20 per pair. On the first pair she made a profit of 25% but on the second pair she suffered a loss of 20%. Did she make a profit altogether?

(9) If 10 men can make 10 cars in 10 days how long will it take 20 men to make 20 cars?

(10) Write down the numbers 1 to 100 in rows:

$$
\begin{array}{cccccccccc}
1 & 2 & 3 & 4 & 5 & 6 & 7 & 8 & 9 & 10 \\
11 & 12 & 13 & 14 & 15 & 16 & 17 & 18 & 19 & 20 \\
21 & 22 & \text{and so on.}
\end{array}
$$

Cross out the 1. Put a circle round 2 and then cross out every other number that divides exactly by 2.
The first of the remaining numbers not circled is 3. Draw a circle round the 3 and cross out every other number that divides by 3. Some are already crossed out. Continue in a similar way for 5, 7 and 11.
The circled numbers are prime numbers. Continue in this way until you can write down all the prime numbers less than 100. Note that 1 is not a prime number.
This is called the Sieve of Eratosthenes.

Exercise 25

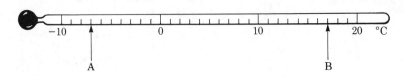

①

(a) What temperature does the arrow A show?
(b) What temperature does the arrow B show?
(c) What is the difference between the two temperatures?

② By placing a decimal point in the correct position, give the 6 in each of the following numbers the value of six hundredths:

(a) 736   (b) 0063   (c) 363.

③ Dean makes up a pattern of numbers starting with 2 and 7. To get the next number in the pattern he adds the previous two numbers together. If the answer is more than 10 he writes down only the number of units. His pattern is 2, 7, 9, 6, ... Write down the next sixty numbers in the pattern. Does the pattern repeat itself? If so how many numbers are repeated?
Now start with 7, 2, . . . and repeat the process.

④ You are offered a two-year contract and a choice of salaries:

either (a) £100 per week plus £5 a week rise after every three months (13 weeks)
or   (b) £105 per week plus £20 a week rise at the end of each year.

Which arrangement would give you more pay over the two years? How much more?

⑤ Looking in the mirror Les sees this reflection of the hall clock. What time is it?

⑥ Sadat thinks his watch is 5 minutes fast when in fact it is 5 minutes slow. Relying on his watch and allowing 5 minutes to spare he arrives for a wedding due to start at 11 a.m. Will he make it?

Given below is a chain of numbers. Each new number is found by writing the difference between the pair of digits above it. The fourth digit is the difference between the first and last digits in the previous line.

$$
\begin{array}{cccc}
6 & 2 & 7 & 4 \\
\ 4 & 5 & 3 & 2\ \\
\ \ 1 & 2 & 1 & 2\ \ \\
\ \ 1 & 1 & 1 & 1\ \ \\
\ \ \ 0 & 0 & 0 & 0\ \ \
\end{array}
$$

Use 3927 to form another similar chain. Now try some numbers that you choose yourself. Compare your results with those of other pupils. What do you notice about the results?

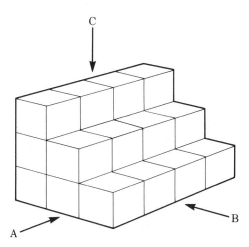

The diagram shows a set of steps that have been made from white plastic cubes of side 20 cm.
(a) Draw the elevation when viewed:
    (i) from direction A   (ii) from direction B.
(b) Draw the plan when viewed from above, i.e from direction C.
(c) How many cubes have been used to make this set of steps?
    (Assume that the view from A shows the uniform cross-section of the solid.)
(d) The solid is painted blue and then taken apart.
    How many of the cubes have:
    (i) four blue faces
    (ii) exactly one blue face
    (iii) four white faces?

(9) Copy this diagram on to squared paper. Draw the reflection of the shaded shape in the mirror line.

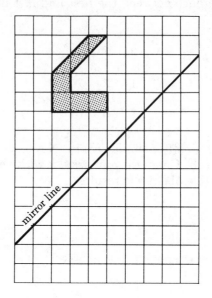

(10)

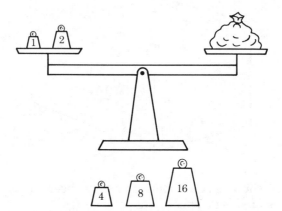

Nicola has a pair of scales and five weights. The weights are 1 kg, 2 kg, 4 kg, 8 kg and 16 kg.

(a) Which weights does she need to weigh:
    (i) 22 kg of wheat   (ii) 14 kg of dog biscuits?

(b) Unfortunately she lost the 4 kg weight. How could she use the remaining weights to weigh:
    (i) 5 kg of carrots   (ii) 14 kg dog biscuits?

(c) Assuming that she did not find the missing 4 kg weight, what whole number values of kilograms between 1 kg and 20 kg inclusive could she *not* weigh?

Exercise 26

1. Five waiters at a restaurant agree to pool their tips and share them equally. One day the tips they receive are £9.60, £12.45, £18.15, £10.60 and £12.20. How much does each get?

2. One day last winter the midday temperature was 8 °C. By midnight the temperature had fallen by 13 °C. What was the temperature at midnight?

3. Use long division to work out the decimal values of all the fractions from $\frac{1}{7}$ to $\frac{6}{7}$ that have 7 as the denominator. Give each one to at least ten decimal places.
   Are any of your answers recurring decimals?
   If so, how many digits are there in each cycle? Is there any link between the different cycles?

4. (a) Jackie and Emma go on a cycling holiday. They hope to cycle 850 miles at the rate of 50 miles per day. How long do they intend to be away?
   (b) After the second day they change their plans. They will rest on the third day, and then cycle and rest on alternate days. How many days are they away?
   (c) Jack and Wayne set out on the same cycling tour but agree that from the beginning they will cycle and rest on alternate days. On cycling days they aim to cycle 60 miles. How long is their holiday?

5.

4	3	4	5
3	3	2	6
8	1	4	3
1	2	2	9

Copy this number square. Starting with the top left-hand square, draw a continuous line, that passes through each square just once, so that the sum of the numbers in each separate block of four consecutive squares is 15.
You can move between squares diagonally as well as up, down or sideways.

(6)

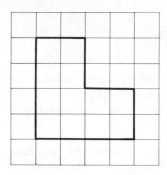

Can you show how to divide this L-shaped allotment into four plots that are all exactly the same size and shape?

(7) Use the signs + − × and ÷ to arrange the first three positive whole numbers to give each of the whole numbers from 1 to 10. All three digits must be used each time. If you wish you can use 2 or 3 as an index.

For example $\dfrac{3}{1+2} = 1$ and $1 + 3^2 = 10$

(8)

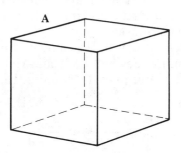

A cube has 6 faces, 8 vertices (or points) and 12 edges. Copy and complete the table on the next page which shows the number of faces, vertices and edges for various other shapes.

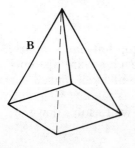

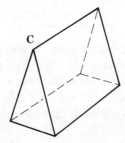

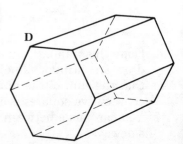

Shape	Number of		
	Faces	Vertices	Edges
A	6	8	12
B			
C			
D			

In each case, name a real object of that shape.

Another object has 16 edges and 9 vertices. Use the information you collected in your table to find out how many faces it has. Can you draw a shape that satisfies this data?

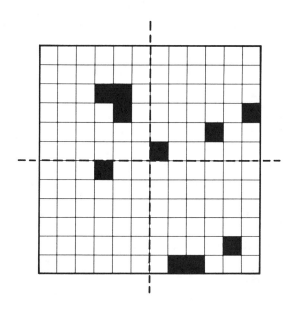

The diagram shows part of a cross-word puzzle. Copy and complete the diagram so that it is symmetrical about both marked axes. How many eight-letter words are there in the cross-word?

⑩ (a) Write down any four-digit number, e.g. 1958. Rearrange the digits in order of size; once so that the largest digit is first and once so that the smallest digit is first,

i.e. 9851 and 1589.

Next find the positive difference between these two numbers,

i.e. 9851 − 1589 = 8262.

Repeat this process for the number 8262,

i.e. 8622 − 2268 = 6354.

These rules have given us a number chain, namely

$$1958 \rightarrow 8262 \rightarrow 6354 \rightarrow$$

Continue this chain for another 5 numbers. What do you notice?
(b) Choose another four-digit number and form a new chain. What do you notice?
(c) Investigate what happens when you choose at least five more four-digit numbers.
(d) You could try the same ideas on some five-digit numbers.

Exercise 27

①

Three cards are shown with numbers on them.
(a) Write down all the 2-figure numbers that can be made using any two of these three cards.
(b) Write down all the three-figure numbers that can be made using all three of these cards.
(c) Put the numbers you found in (b) in order of size, smallest first.

② Write down the next five lines in this pattern.

$$
\begin{aligned}
1 &= 1 \\
1 + 2 &= 3 \\
1 + 2 + 3 &= 6 \\
1 + 2 + 3 + 4 &= 10
\end{aligned}
$$

Can you work out what the total would be for:
(a) the 12th line   (b) the 20th line?

③ The table shows the number of meals served by a works canteen during a particular week.

Mon	Tues	Wed	Thurs	Fri
215	197	242	209	128

(a) How many meals did this canteen serve during the five days?
(b) The canteen was also open on Saturday. The total number of meals served on the six days was 1079. How many meals were served on Saturday?

68

④ At a county sports meeting there are 64 entries for the 100 metres. There are 8 lanes.

(a) If the first four in any race are allowed to go on to the next round, what is the least number of races necessary to find the winner?

(b) How many times must the eventual winner race?

⑤ (a) Kim asked Flo the value of 2^4 and the value of 3^3. Flo said that the value of 2^4 was $2 \times 2 \times 2 \times 2$, i.e. 16, and that the value of 3^3 was $3 \times 3 \times 3$, i.e. 27. Was Flo correct?

(b) What is the value of:
(i) 4^2 (ii) 5^3 (iii) 3^4?

⑥ Two sisters and a brother go out for a meal. They agree to share the total cost of £24.36 equally, but the brother finds that he has left his money at home. How much extra must each of his sisters pay in order to cover their brother's share of the bill?

⑦

The diagram above shows the prices of two jars of coffee.

(a) What is the cost of 25 g from the smaller jar?
(b) What is the cost of 25 g from the larger jar?
(c) Which jar is the better value?
(d) The company brings out a new even larger jar containing 250 g priced at £3.70. Is this better value for money than either of the other two?

⑧ Mrs Wellfield sells duck eggs every Tuesday in the local market. Last Tuesday without breaking any eggs she sold half of what she had plus half an egg to her first customer. To her second customer she sold half of what remained plus half an egg. That left her with 4 duck eggs. How many did she have to start with?

⑨ Sue, Nita, Mags and Hazel are four sisters. Mags is twice as old as Sue. The eldest is looking forward to becoming a teenager soon. Nita is half Hazel's age and is two years older than Mags. How old is each sister?

69

(10)

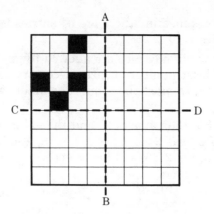

This layout for a cross-word is to be symmetrical about each of the lines AB and CD. Copy the grid on to squared paper and complete the shading. How many: (a) three-letter words (b) eight-letter words, will there be?

Exercise 28

(1) One day last Summer, sunrise was at 0642 and sunset was at 1932. How long was the sun up?

(2) How would you make up £1 using 20 coins including a 50 p piece?

(3)

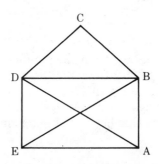

Copy the 'envelope' without lifting your pencil from the paper and without going over any line twice. Start at A.
One possible way is

How many more can you find that start at A?
Now try starting at B.
How many of the points A, B, C, D and E is it possible to start from and succeed?

70

(4) Tina decides to take a 20-lesson swimming course. She starts the course on Saturday 1 June and has a lesson every fourth day. What will be the date and day of the week when she has her final lesson?

(5) If two hens lay two eggs in two days how long should it take six hens to lay six eggs?

(6)

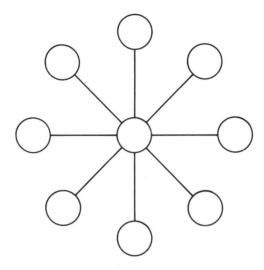

Put the digits 1 to 9 into these nine circles so that the sum of every three numbers lying on a straight line adds up to 15.

(7) Wazim has 50 p and Aziz has 40 p. How much must Aziz give Wazim so that Wazim has twice as much as Aziz?

(8) Five grown-up brothers and sisters meet at a family gathering. Each one shakes hands with each of the other four. How many hand shakes are there?
What would the answer be if there were six brothers and sisters?

(9)

3	2	7
6	5	4
9	8	1

This square shows the digits from 1 to 9 arranged in such a way that the three-figure number in the second row is twice the number in the first row and the number in the third row is the sum of the numbers in the other two rows. There are three other ways of arranging the nine digits to give the same result. Can you find any of them?

(10)

(a) Sam bought two different items at the sale and paid £41. What did he buy?

(b) Judy bought two of the same article and had £2 change when she paid with two £20 notes. What did she buy?

(c) Trish spent £60 on three different items. What did she buy?

(d) Which is the more expensive and by how much:
two dresses and a pair of shoes or
two sweaters, a skirt, a T-shirt and a radio?

Exercise 29 A

① A wine glass holds 150 ml. How many glasses can be filled:
(a) from a 1 litre bottle of wine
(b) from a 70 centilitre bottle of wine?

② Three 6s can be used to make 30

e.g. $6 \times 6 - 6 = 30.$

Can you find any other digit that, when used three times, together with two of the signs + − × ÷, gives the same result of 30?

③ At the moment Nelson is three times as old as Sutton. In four years' time Sutton will be half Nelson's age.
(a) How old is Sutton now?
(b) How old will Nelson be in 10 years' time?

(4) If Sajida buys three attached stamps, how many different lay-outs can they have? Illustrate your answer with sketches.

(5) Look at this pattern

$$1^2 + 2^2 = 3^2 - 2^2$$
$$2^2 + 3^2 = 7^2 - 6^2$$
$$3^2 + 4^2 = 13^2 - 12^2$$

Give the next five lines of this pattern.
Verify that each line is correct.

(6) The attendance at an international match is 64 749. What is this:
(a) correct to the nearest thousand
(b) correct to the nearest hundred
(c) correct to three significant figures
(d) correct to the nearest ten thousand?

(7) A cyclist covers 750 m on each complete lap of a track in a stadium. How many complete laps must she cycle to cover 12 kilometres?

(8) Tommy Ricketts wants to pave a rectangular area using square slabs, each with an area of one square metre. He has the same number of yellow slabs as he has red slabs. He decides to put all the red slabs at the boundary of the rectangle and all the yellow slabs inside these. Show a possible arrangement. How many slabs does he have? What are the dimensions of the rectangular area that he covers?

(9) (a)

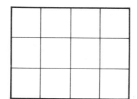

The sketch shows an aerial view of a cardboard box that will hold 12 bottles.
Can you put eight bottles into this box so that each row and each column of the box has an *even* number of bottles in it? Is there more than one way of doing it?
(Accept 0, 2, 4 as even for the sake of this question.)
(b) If you found part (a) interesting, try putting 12 bottles into a square box that has 4 rows and 4 columns, i.e. can hold 16 bottles. Once again there must be an even number of bottles in each row and in each column. There are lots of acceptable ways of doing this.

73

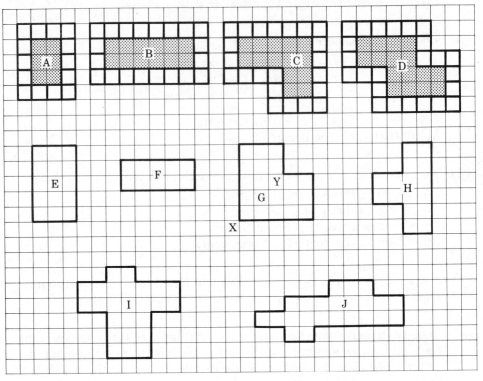

Claude works for a landscape gardener and specialises in laying paving slabs around lawns, flower beds and ponds. All the slabs he uses are square and have an area of one square foot. Different shapes of flower beds are shown in diagrams A to J.

(a) Bed A measures 3 ft by 2 ft. How many slabs does Claude need to go around the edge of this?
(b) For bed B write down:
   (i) its overall length and breadth
   (ii) the number of slabs needed to go all the way round it.
(c) For bed C the overall width of the bed is 4 ft and the overall length is 5 ft. What is its perimeter? How many slabs are needed to go all the way round?
(d) How many more slabs do you need to go round an 'outside' corner like X, in bed G, than round an 'inside' corner like Y?
(e) For flowerbed D
   (i) What is its overall length and width?
   (ii) How many slabs are needed to go around its edge?
   (iii) How many outside corners does it have?
   (iv) How many inside corners does it have?
(f) Repeat part (e) for each of the beds from E to J.

(g) Copy the table given below and write your answers to the previous parts of the question in it.

Diagram	Overall Width	Length	Perimeter	No. of outside corners	No. of inside corners	Total number of slabs required
A						
B						
C						
D						
E						
F						
G						
H						
I						
J						

(h) Can you see any connection between the numbers in the last four columns?

Exercise 30

① Write 37.084:
(a) correct to the nearest 10
(b) correct to three significant figures
(c) correct to one decimal place.

② If a bag containing £20 in 50 p pieces weighs 530 grams, what is the weight of one 50 p piece? (Neglect the weight of the bag.)

③ If Ed buys four attached first-class stamps, how many different lay-outs can they have?

④ Tim, Steve, Paul and Malcolm are four brothers with a total age of 57 years. Steve is twice as old as Malcolm. Tim is one year younger than Steve. Malcolm is the only one who has not yet become a teenager and he is ten years younger than Paul. How old is each brother?

(5)

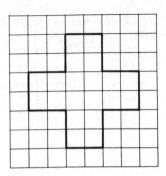

On squared paper draw a Greek cross that has an area of 20 squares. Cut off four identical pieces from this cross and rearrange the five pieces to form a square.

(6)

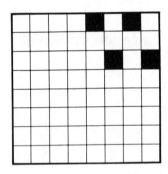

This cross-word puzzle is to have rotational symmetry of order four about its centre. Copy the diagram on to squared paper and complete the shading.

How many seven-letter words are there in this cross-word?

(7)

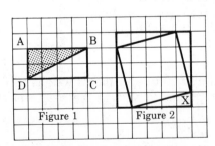

Figure 1   Figure 2

In the diagrams, each small square represents an area of 1 square metre.

(a) In Figure 1, find:
   (i) the area of the rectangle ABCD
   (ii) the area of the shaded triangle.
(b) In Figure 2, find:
   (i) the area of the large square

(ii) the area of the triangle marked X

(iii) the area of the inner square.

(c) Use the ideas you found helpful in parts (a) and (b) to find the area represented by each of the following squares:

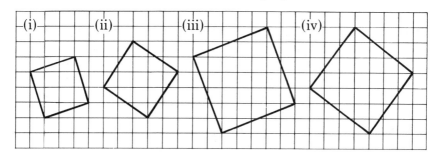

⑧

1	2	3	4	5	6	7	8	9	10
11	12	13	14	15	16	17	18	19	20
21	22	23	24	25	26	27	28	29	30
31	32	33	34	35	36	37	38	39	40
41	42	43	44	45	46	47	48	49	50
51	52	53	54	55	56	57	58	59	60
61	62	63	64	65	66	67	68	69	70
71	72	73	74	75	76	77	78	79	80
81	82	83	84	85	86	87	88	89	90
91	92	93	94	95	96	97	98	99	100

(a) Select any 2 × 2 square, for example

44	45
54	55

Multiply the pairs of numbers at the opposite corners, and find the difference between the two answers.

In our example, $44 \times 55 = 2420$

and $54 \times 45 = 2430$.

The difference is therefore 10.

Try similar calculations for some squares of four numbers that you choose from the 1 to 100 square given above. What do you notice about the results?

(b) Try a similar thing using the numbers at the corners of a 3 × 3 square.

For example, if we use the square

12	13	14
22	23	24
32	33	34

the products would be $12 \times 34 = 408$.

and $14 \times 32 = 448$.

Hence the diference is 40.

77

(c) What happens for a 4 × 4 square and then a 5 × 5 square?

(d) Can you suggest what the answer would be for a 6 × 6 square and a 7 × 7 square. Confirm these by choosing first a 6 × 6 square and then a 7 × 7 square, and doing the calculations for each.

(9) Last year Sigma Industries gave every employee a Christmas hamper. Each hamper contained 'goodies' to the same value. The total cost of these hampers was £1369. How many employees were there? What was the value of each hamper?

(Assume that each hamper cost an exact number of pounds.)

(10) The sequence 1, 3, 4, 7, 11, 18, 29, . . . is called a Lucas sequence. Select any number in the sequence other than 1. Multiply the number you have selected by itself. Next multiply its two neighbours together. For example, if 7 is chosen:

$$7 \times 7 = 49 \text{ and } 4 \times 11 = 44.$$

Finally find the difference between these two values. In our chosen example the difference is $49 - 44 = 5$.

Repeat this for all the numbers in the given sequence. What do you notice about the results? Can you use the results you have just obtained to work out the next five terms in a Lucas sequence?

Exercise 31 == (A)

(1) John has a three-metre length of copper tube. He cuts off three half-metre lengths. Each cut consumes one millimetre of tube. How much copper tube remains? How many more half-metre lengths can still be cut off? How much is John short of the amount needed to make another one?

(2)

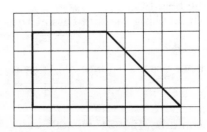

Show how to divide this trapezium into four identical pieces. You will find squared paper useful for this question.

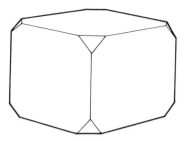

A wooden cube has all its corners cut off (as shown in the diagram) leaving an equilateral triangle at each corner. For the resulting solid, find the number of faces, edges and vertices.
Use your results to check Euler's relation which says that:

number of faces + number of vertices − number of edges = 2

④

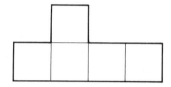

One more square needs to be added to this net so that when it is cut out it can be folded to form a cube. Copy this diagram and show all the possible positions in which the square can be added.

⑤ Ray Sedgemoor left Heathrow airport at 11 a.m. local time to fly to San Francisco. He arrived in San Francisco at 1 p.m. local time. If San Francisco time is 8 hours behind London time, how long did the flight take?

⑥ Two brothers, David and Nathan, join the same firm as engineers but agree to different salary arrangements. David agrees to an annual salary of £10 000, plus a rise of £500 every six months. Nathan agrees to the same starting salary but his increase is to be £2000 at the end of every two years. How much does each brother earn during the first five years? Which one secures the better deal?

⑦ In a golf tournament of four rounds, the expected score, or par score, for each round is 72.
   (a) In the first three rounds a player scores 73, 69 and 70. What must he score in the final round if he is to finish on par for the tournament?
   (b) A score of 69 is described as 3 under par for the round, i.e. 72 − 69 = 3. Another player has scores of 72, 68 and 71 for his first three rounds. How many under par is he for the tournament at this stage? At the end of the tournament he was 1 over par. What was his fourth round score?

(8) If 6 women can make 12 dresses in 3 days how long will it take 12 women to make 8 dresses?

(9)

7		6	-7
		3	
		-6	5
	1	-1	4

Copy and complete this number square. The sum of the numbers in each column, row and diagonal must always be the same.

(10) A palindrome is a number that reads the same whether it is written backwards or forwards,

e.g.   44, 1221, 53935.

(a) Write down all the two-figure numbers that are palindromes.
(b) Write down any two-figure number that is not a palindrome, for example 53. Now write this number down backwards, i.e. 35, and add it to the first number.
53 + 35 = 88 which is a palindrome.
Find some other two-figure numbers that give palindromes in this way.
(c) Some two-figure numbers do not give palindromes. When added to the number written backwards
e.g. 67 + 76 = 143 which is not a palindrome.
However, if we repeat the process we used in (b) with 143 we get
143 + 341 = 484 which is a palindrome.
Find some two-figure numbers that give palindromes in this way, i.e. by repeating the process twice.
(d) If you repeat the process enough times does 87 give a palindrome?

Exercise 32 ══════════════════════════ **A**

(1) Estimate the reading on each of these scales.

(a)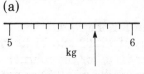

(b)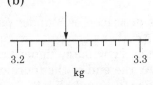

(c)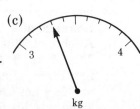

80

Two jars of Cranston pickle are shown above. What is the cost of each, per gram? Give each answer correct to three decimal places. Which one is the better value for money?

③ The English department wishes to transport 162 fifth-form pupils plus 16 teachers, to London, which is 90 miles away, to attend a concert at the Albert Hall. The local bus company has two kinds of coaches, 29-seaters and 42-seaters. Fuel consumption is 15 m.p.g. for the smaller coach and 12 m.p.g. for the larger one. Fuel costs £2 per gallon and all drivers are paid £35 a day.

(a) How many gallons of fuel are used for this trip by
   (i) a 29-seater   (ii) a 42-seater?
(b) What is the total cost of hiring each type of coach for this journey?
(c) How many 29-seater coaches are needed if it is decided to use three 42-seaters?
(d) What combination of coaches provide the cheapest way of hiring coaches for this school trip? How much does this work out at per pupil if the teachers travel free? Give your answer correct to the nearest 5 p, rounded upwards.

④

$$2 \times 2 - 1 \times 1 = 3$$
$$3 \times 3 - 2 \times 2 = 5$$
$$4 \times 4 - 3 \times 3 = 7$$
$$5 \times 5 - 4 \times 4 = 9$$

(a) Write down the next six lines in this pattern.
(b) Write down the 50th line in this pattern.

⑤ The square of 2 is $2^2 = 2 \times 2 = 4$
and the cube of 2 is $2^3 = 2 \times 2 \times 2 = 8$.
4 is therefore a perfect square since $4 = 2 \times 2$
and 8 is a perfect cube since $8 = 2 \times 2 \times 2$.
What is the smallest number, greater than 1, that is both a perfect square and a perfect cube?

⑥

6	4	8	1	2
4	4	5	1	7
1	3	2	2	1
2	9	10	5	9
2	1	4	4	3

Copy this number square and, starting in the top left-hand square, draw a continuous line passing through each square just once so that the sum of the numbers in each new group of five consecutive squares is 20.

⑦

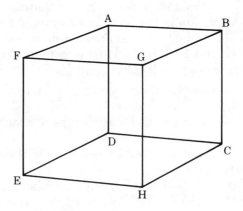

A spider rests at A, one vertex of the outline of a cube that has been made from a length of wire. It wants to get to H. It must walk only along the wire; it cannot walk along any edge more than once; it is not allowed to walk upwards and it cannot return to A. One possible route is ABCH. How many other routes are there? Describe them in a similar way.

⑧ On a separate sheet of paper try to draw each of these shapes without lifting the pencil from the paper and without going over any line twice. You can start at any point. Keep the failed drawings as well as the successful ones.

(a) 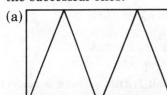 (b) 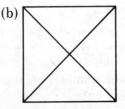 (c)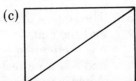

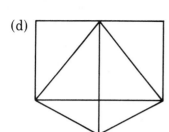

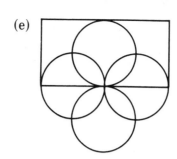

(d)   (e)

---

9 The numbers 3, 4 and 5 are related in a rather special way since
$3^2 + 4^2 = 5^2$. When three sides of a triangle have lengths 3 units,
4 units and 5 units the triangle contains a right angle and the three
numbers 3, 4 and 5 form what is called a Pythagorean triple. There
are many other Pythagorean triples,
e.g. 5, 12 and 13, since $5^2 + 12^2 = 13^2$ $(25 + 144 = 169)$
and 6, 8 and 10, since $6^2 + 8^2 = 10^2$ $(36 + 64 = 100)$.
Complete the following table. For each triple the smallest number is
written in the first column and the largest number is written in the
third column. Columns four to six give the squares of these numbers.
The sum of the numbers in column four and column five must give
the number in column six.

Column no.

1	2	3	4	5	6
a	b	c	a^2	b^2	c^2
3	4	5	9	16	25
5	12	13	25	144	169
6					
7	24				
8		17			
9	12	15	81	144	225
9	40	41	81	1600	1681
10					
11					
12					
12					
13		85			
14					
15					
15					

There are of course very many more Pythagorean triples. Can you
find more? Can you find a pattern or patterns that will enable you to
find more?

(10) While on holiday in Majorca, Karin was coming down in the lift. She was looking into the mirror at the back of the lift and saw a reflection of the controls. It looked as though they had stopped at floor 5. Which floor had they stopped at?

On another occasion the reflection in the mirror looked as though they had stopped at floor 51. What floor was it this time?

Exercise 33

For questions 1 to 4 to have any value you must observe the instructions.

(1) *Without turning the page around,* try to draw each of these letters as you would see it upside down.

(2) *Without turning the page around,* draw each of these shapes as they would appear upside down.

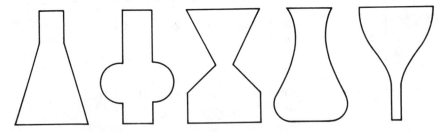

(3) Draw each of these patterns as they would appear if you looked at them upside down. Squared paper is useful but not essential.

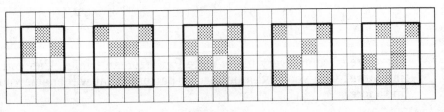

④ In this question do not turn the page around until you have completed the question.

Draw each shape as it would look if it was turned about the point marked with an X:

(a) through $\frac{1}{4}$ turn clockwise

(b) through $\frac{1}{2}$ turn clockwise

(c) through $\frac{3}{4}$ turn clockwise.

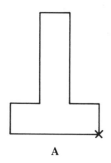

A

B

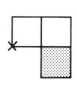

C

⑤ Use some or all of the digits from 1 to 9 *in order*, separated by + or − or × or ÷, to try to make as many numbers as you can from 1 to 30,

e.g. $4 = 12 \div 3$ and $29 = 34 - 5$.

⑥ How many different squares are there on an 8 × 8 chess board? Remember that you can have squares of different sizes.

⑦ The list below shows the positions of the top six clubs in a Volleyball League at the end of November:

1 Bardley
2 Caxton
3 Finchdown
4 Greenborough
5 Central
6 Darlin

Two weeks later several changes had occurred:
Greenborough were top;
Caxton were immediately above Bardley;
Finchdown had been replaced by Eastly in the top six;
Darlin were immediately below Bardley;
Central's position was unchanged.
Show the position of the top six clubs in the league after taking these changes into account.

⑧ Julie bought a car for £10 000. Each year it lost one-fifth of its value at the beginning of that year. What was it worth:

(a) when it was three years old
(b) when it was five years old?

⑨ Mrs Dale went to see a friend and walked at a steady speed. She stayed at the friend's house for a short while and then walked home again at the same steady speed. Which of the following graphs best represents her journey?

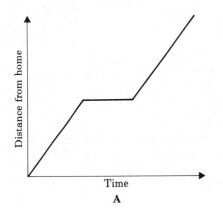

A

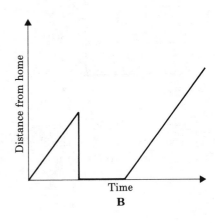

B

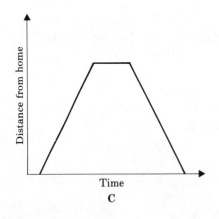

C

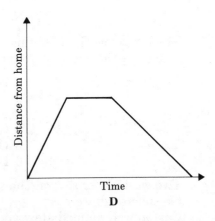

D

⑩ (a) By subtracting the areas of triangles from the appropriate rectangle find the area of each of the triangles A, B and C. Each small square represents 1 cm².

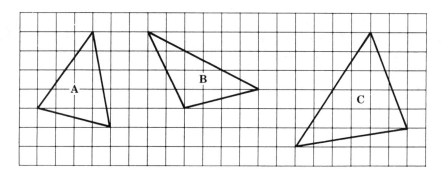

(b) Find the area of each of these triangular fields if each small square represent 1 hectare.

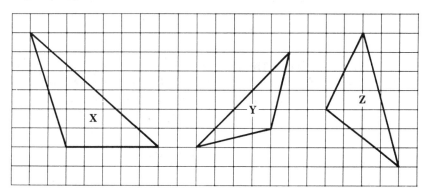

Exercise 34

① The school running track has eight lanes. Thirty pupils enter for the 100 metres. How would you organise the heats to get the eight pupils for the final?

② (a) How many squares are there in this figure?
(b) How many of these squares contain an ×?
(c) How many contain an ○?

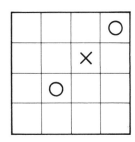

③ Max Kaufman buys a new car. He estimates that he can drive 28 000 miles with any given tyre before it needs renewing. How far should he be able to drive his new car before he needs to buy any new tyres? (Don't forget the spare!)

Four girls went on holiday together. Three of them spent exactly £100 each but Jane spent £15 more than the average for the four of them. How much did Jane spend?

⑤

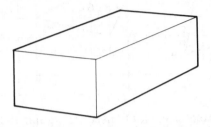

Pauline has a rectangular block of Cheddar cheese. What is the least number of cuts she must make in order to cut this block of cheese into eight identical pieces?

⑥ The string section of the Boscombe Symphony Orchestra consists of first violins, second violins, violas, 'cellos and double basses. There are always two more 'cellos than double basses, two more violas than 'cellos, two more second violins than violas and two more first violins than second violins.
(a) The first half of a concert requires eight double basses. How many players will there be in the string section?
(b) The second half of the concert requires four double basses. How many of the string players who performed in the first half of the concert are not required for the second half? How many remain?

⑦

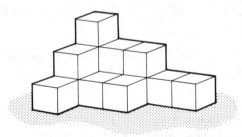

(a) How many small cubes have been used to make this stack?
(b) If each cube has a volume of one cubic centimetre, calculate the total surface area of this stack that is exposed.

⑧ Bill Collins had some very strange ideas when it came to putting ten fencing posts up. He put them in five rows with four posts in each row. When he stretched wire between them he was able to enclose a regular pentagon which included ten isosceles triangles. Can you find out how he arranged the posts? (No area is in more than one triangle.)

⑨ Rita has 60 p and Olive has £1. How much must Rita give Olive so that Olive has three times as much as Rita?

⑩

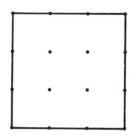

Mark 16 dots and draw a square around them as shown in the diagram.

Join dots by straight lines to show how this square can be divided into two identical pieces. There are many ways of doing this. Two of them are given below.

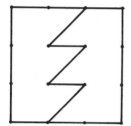 

Exercise 35

① Joe's cooking instructions for roasting chicken say that he should allow 15 minutes per pound plus 20 minutes extra.

  (a) How much time should Joe allow to cook a 5 lb chicken?
  (b) He wants it to be ready by 6.45 p.m. What time should he put it in the oven?

②

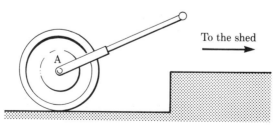

To the shed

Larry pulls his garden roller along a level path, up a step and towards the garden shed. Show the path traced out by the centre of the roller, A, as he does this.

③ The weekly rental for a television set is £14. The cash price for the same set is £320. For how many weeks can the set be hired before the cost is greater than buying the set outright?

④ A street is 1 kilometre long. Street lamps are placed down one side every 100 m starting from one end. Down the other side they are also placed every 100 m but starting 50 m from one end. How many lamps are there altogether in the street?

⑤ Sally noticed that

$$1 + 2 + 1 = 4 = 2^2$$
$$1 + 2 + 3 + 2 + 1 = 9 = 3^2$$
$$1 + 2 + 3 + 4 + 3 + 2 + 1 = 16 = 4^2.$$

Without counting up all the numbers, what is the value of:

(a) $1 + 2 + 3 + 4 + 5 + 6 + 7 + 8 + 7 + 6 + 5 + 4 + 3 + 2 + 1$
(b) $1 + 2 + 3 + \ldots 49 + 50 + 49 + \ldots + 3 + 2 + 1$
(c) $1 + 2 + 3 + \ldots 99 + 100 + 99 + \ldots + 3 + 2 + 1?$

⑥ Six skirts are offered for sale in the window of a department store. Their prices are £13, £15, £20, £24, £28 and £29. The first customer buys two skirts, and the second customer buys three skirts, but in so doing spends twice as much as the first customer.

(a) What are the prices of the skirts the first customer buys?
(b) What are the prices of the skirts the second customer buys?
(c) What is the price of the skirt left unsold?

⑦ A motorist travels 161 miles in $3\frac{1}{2}$ hours.

(a) Find his average speed for this journey.
(b) His car will travel 44 miles on each gallon of petrol. What is the least number of gallons of petrol he needs to complete the journey?
(c) His journey starts at 9.45 a.m. At what time should he arrive?

⑧ A bill for £260 is paid using £5 and £20 notes. If there are three times as many £20 notes as £5 notes how many of each are paid?

⑨ The number 6 is a perfect number since the sum of all its factors, 1, 2, 3, 6, is double the number itself.
Show that 24 is a perfect number.
One of the numbers 492, 494 and 496 is a perfect number. Can you find which one it is?

(10)

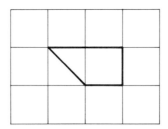

This shape was obtained by folding another shape along a line of symmetry.
Possible shapes that it could come from are:

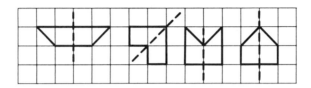

Find all the different shapes from which each of the following shapes can be obtained by folding along a line of symmetry.

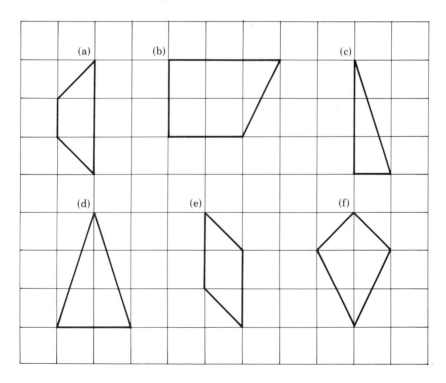

This shape was obtained by folding a shape along a line of symmetry and then folding it again along a line of symmetry of the resulting shape. Draw the original shape.

91

Exercise 36

① A puppy weighs 100 g when it is born and doubles its weight every week for the first five weeks. What does it weigh:

(a) when it is three weeks old
(b) when it is five weeks old?

② How many times in 12 hours do the hands of a clock point in the same direction?

③ Use long multiplication to find the value of 11 × 11, 111 × 111 and 1111 × 1111. Can you see a pattern? Use this pattern to write down, without using a calculator or long multiplication, the value of:

(a) 11 111 × 11 111   (b) 111 111 × 111 111.

④ A smallholder has some chickens and some pens. If three chickens are put in each pen, two chickens are left over. If four chickens are put in each pen, one pen is empty. How many chickens and how many pens are there?

⑤ A goat is tethered to the mid-point of the boundary wall of a square field of side 100 m. The tether is 10 m long. The shape of the area of grass that the goat can eat is:

A a square   **B** a rectangle   **C** a semi-circle   **D** a triangle?

⑥

Two discs are shown with numbers on them. Each disc has a different prime number on the back from the one on the front. The sum of all four numbers is 26 and the sum of the two numbers on the first disc is one more than one of the numbers on the second disc. Write down all the two-figure numbers you can make by laying these two discs on the desk.

⑦ Spanish olive oil can be bought in bottles in the supermarket in four different sizes:

$\frac{1}{4}$ litre   90 p
$\frac{1}{2}$ litre   125 p
1 litre   225 p
2 litres   430 p

Yvonne needs $1\frac{3}{4}$ litre of oil. What is the cheapest way of buying it?

How can two wooden cubes be numbered, using a single number on each face, so that it is possible to display all the dates on a calendar from 1 to 31. The two blocks must be used to form every number so that the first of the month is shown as

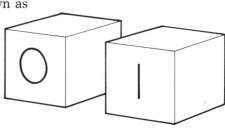

⑨

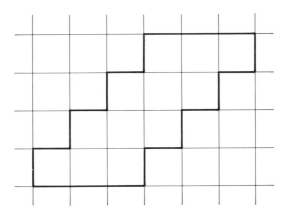

On centimetre squared or dotted paper, draw three different rectangles and four different right-angled triangles that each have an area equal to the shape drawn above. The sides of the rectangles, and the length of the base and perpendicular height of each triangle, must be an exact number of centimetres.
Is the perimeter of any shape you have drawn equal to the perimeter of the given shape?
How many shapes have a longer perimeter than the given shape?

(10) The Thomson family each enjoy half a grapefruit for breakfast every morning. There are five members of the family. David spends three nights at home at the weekend, and Jane is at home every Friday night and Saturday night otherwise they are away. When Mrs Thomson leaves to do her shopping on Friday morning there are no grapefruit at home.

(a) What is the smallest number of grapefruit she must buy to meet the needs of the family for the next seven days?

(b) Assuming that the grapefruit are always prepared the previous evening, on how many days would there be an unused 'half' in the fridge?

Exercise 37 ⸺⸺⸺⸺⸺⸺⸺ **A**

(1) The liner *Sea Princess* left Southampton on the morning of Saturday 23 June for a 14-night cruise in the Mediterranean. On what date did it return? What day of the week was this?

(2)

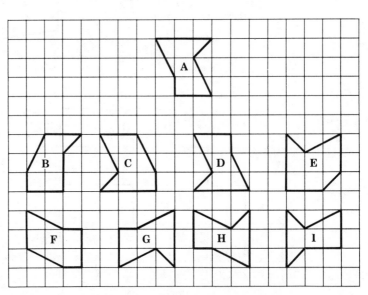

Which shapes are exactly the same size as shape A?

(3) Work out these patterns without using a calculator.

(a) (1 × 8) + 1   =
    (12 × 8) + 2   =
    (123 × 8) + 3   =
    (1234 × 8) + 4   =
    (12 345 × 8) + 5 =

(b) 1 × 9 + 2   =
    12 × 9 + 3   =
    123 × 9 + 4   =
    1234 × 9 + 5   =
    12 345 × 9 + 6 =

(c) Use the patterns you have found in parts (a) and (b) to write down the value of:
   (i) $(12\,345\,678 \times 8) + 8$
   (ii) $12\,345\,678 \times 9 + 9$.

 4 Suppose you have the following eight coins:
1 p, 2 p, 2 p, 5 p, 10 p, 20 p, 20 p, 50 p.
Can you pay a bill for any sum less than £1 without being given change?

5

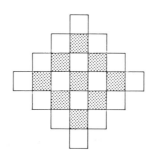

Look at this tiling pattern.
(a) How many white tiles are there?
(b) How many black tiles are there?
(c) How many tiles are there altogether?
(d) What is the greatest number of tiles, black and white, in any one row?
(e) The squares of which two consecutive whole numbers can be added to give the answer to part (c)?
(f) What is the sum of the squares of these two whole numbers?
(g) How does this compare with the total number of tiles used?
(h) Repeat parts (a) to (g) for this pattern.

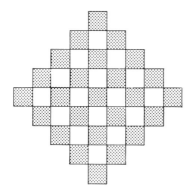

(i) Suppose a similar pattern has 13 squares as the greatest number of tiles in a single row. Without drawing a diagram, try to answer parts (a) to (g) again for this pattern.

The perimeter of the rectangle shown above is 6 cm and the area is 2 cm^2, i.e. the number of units of area (A) $= \frac{1}{3} \times$ the number of units of the length of the perimeter (P),

i.e. $\qquad\qquad\qquad\qquad\qquad A = \frac{1}{3}P.$

Can you draw a rectangle for which:

(a) $A = P$ (b) $A = 2P$ (c) $A = \frac{1}{2}P$ (d) $A = 4P$?

(You can attempt to do this question by trial and improvement and/ or by forming equations.)

(7) George pays a bill for £105 using only £5 and £10 notes. There are fourteen notes altogether. How many of each type of note are there?

(8) Molly earns £120 per week. She gives 25% of this to her mother and saves one-third of the remainder.

(a) How much does she give to her mother?
(b) How much does she save?
(c) How much remains for her to spend?

(9)

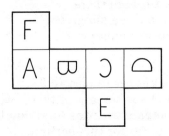

The letters A to F are drawn on the net for a cube as shown in the diagram above.

This net is folded to form a cube. The cube is next placed inside a fixed open transparent cubical box. One possible way is shown below.

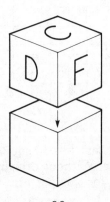

Some of the other possible ways of sliding the cube into the box are given below, but one face is left blank. Copy each drawing and fill in the blank face with the appropriate letter in the correct position.

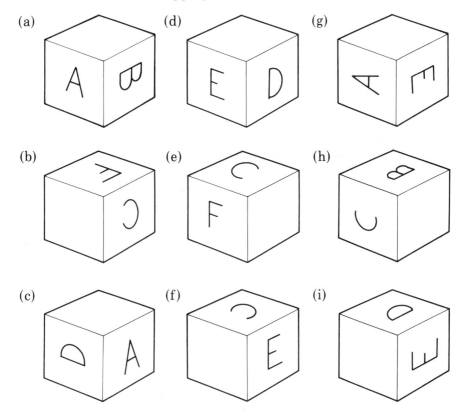

(a)   (d)   (g)

(b)   (e)   (h)

(c)   (f)   (i)

(j) Is it possible to place the cube in the box so that the letters on the four vertical faces are upright? Illustrate your answer with a diagram.

(k) Give a net for this cube so that all six letters are drawn on the net in an upright position.

(l) Parts (a) to (i) show nine different ways of putting the cube into the box. How many different ways are there of putting the cube into the box so that A is in contact with the base of the box? How many different ways are there of putting the cube into the box?

(10) When a snooker ball bounces against the cushion of a snooker table the angle at which it comes on to the cushion is equal to the angle at which it leaves the cushion.

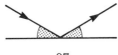

Any ball that hits the cushion at an angle of 45° with it, leaves the cushion at the same angle.

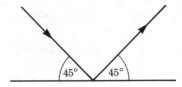

Study this diagram of a small table which is two thirds as wide as it is long and which has pockets at the four corners. Suppose a snooker ball starts at 1 at an angle of 45° with the cushion. Its path is shown in the diagram. It will disappear down the pocket at 9.

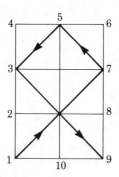

If a ball starts at 2 ($\frac{1}{3}$ of the way along one side) and rolls at 45° with the upward direction of the cushion, it will disappear down the pocket at 6, but if it rolls at 45° with the downward direction of the cushion it will disappear down the pocket at 4 (see the diagram below).

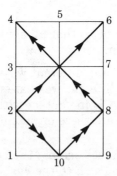

(a) Draw diagrams to show how the ball rolls before it disappears down a pocket if it starts at any point where there is a number. Remember that at all points except the corners there are two possible starting directions.

98

(b) Can the ball be pocketed irrespective of the number at which it starts?

(c) Is the total distance the ball travels before it is pocketed constant for all the starting points? Remember that if a ball starts from a point other than a corner there are two routes to a pocket.

Exercise 38

① The distance around the edge of one square table mat in a set of six is 80 cm.

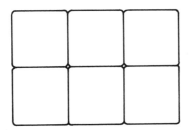

All six mats in the set are placed together as shown in the sketch. What is the distance around the edge of this shape?

② In each case write down the value shown by the pointer.

(a)

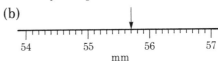

(b)

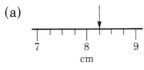

(c)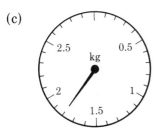

(d)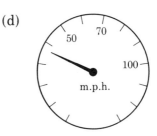

③ One day last winter, the street lights were switched on at 1632 and switched off at 0718 the next day. How long were the street lights on for that night?

④ A safe can be opened by the correct combination of four digits.
When 5648 is tried two digits are wrong,
when 3628 is tried two digits are wrong,
when 3148 is tried two digits are wrong
and when 5629 is tried two digits are wrong.
What is the correct four-digit combination that opens the safe?

⑤ Which of these nets cannot be folded to form a cube?

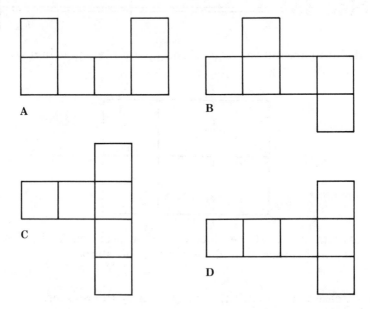

⑥ Alf has a 4 metre length of wood. His saw makes a sawcut
2 millimetres wide. He cuts the wood into five equal lengths. How
long is each piece?
What is the length of each piece if he cuts the 4 metre piece into ten
equal pieces?

⑦ The time in Moscow is three hours ahead of the time in London,
while the time in London is five hours ahead of the time in New
York. What time is it:

(a) in London when it is 5 a.m. in Moscow
(b) in London when it is 10 p.m. in New York
(c) in New York when it is 2 p.m. in Moscow?

(8) This chart shows the distances, in miles, between several places in the United Kingdom.

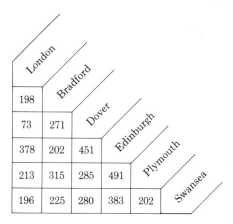

London	Bradford	Dover	Edinburgh	Plymouth	Swansea
198					
73	271				
378	202	451			
213	315	285	491		
196	225	280	383	202	

(a) How far is it from London to Edinburgh?
(b) How far is it from Swansea to Dover?
(c) Which two places are furthest apart?
(d) Which two places are closest together?
(e) How far is it from London to Edinburgh via Bradford?
(f) How far is it from Plymouth to Dover via London?
(g) Terry averages 40 m.p.h. on a journey from Plymouth to Swansea. About how long should this journey take?
(h) Wendy averages 40 m.p.h. when she is actually driving but always has a 30 minute break after every 100 miles. About how long should she take to drive from Edinburgh to Swansea?

(9) Alderbridge and Blackwood are 26 miles apart. Signposts are placed every mile along the road. Each signpost shows the distance to each town, for example

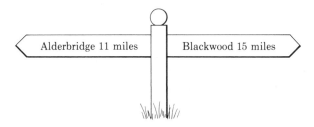

The distances on this signpost are made up using just two digits, namely 1 and 5.

(a) How many signposts are needed, including the one in Alderbridge and the one in Blackwood?
(b) How many of the signposts *between* the two towns use exactly two digits (including zeros)?

101

(c) How many of the signposts between the two towns use exactly three digits?

(d) How many times is the digit 1 used?

(e) How many times is the digit 8 used?

(f) A painter is paid £1 for each digit he paints. How much does he earn if he paints all the digits on the signposts from Alderbridge to Blackwood?

⑩ A cricket league has 12 teams. Each team plays each of the other teams twice; once at home and once away. Games are played on Wednesdays and Saturdays.

(a) How many games should be played altogether?

(b) What is the least number of weeks that the season lasts?

(c) If another two teams join the league how many extra games will need to be played?

Exercise 39 ==================================

① Twins, Laura and Lavinia, go to a restaurant for a meal with their elder brother Bob. The total cost is £29.32 but Bob agrees to pay twice as much as each of the twins. How much does Lavinia pay?

② A businessman leaves Heathrow airport, London, at 12 noon local time and arrives at Kennedy airport, New York, at 2 p.m. local time. If New York time is five hours behind London time how long is the flight?

③ On a calculator Sim is told that he can use only the keys $\boxed{3}$ $\boxed{4}$ $\boxed{\times}$ $\boxed{-}$ $\boxed{=}$, but he can press them as often as he wishes. To get 6 he can press

$\boxed{3}$ $\boxed{\times}$ $\boxed{4}$ $\boxed{-}$ $\boxed{3}$ $\boxed{-}$ $\boxed{3}$ $\boxed{=}$ or $3 \times 4 - 3 - 3 =$ for short.

He can also get 6 by pressing $3 \times 3 - 3 =$

(a) Can you find two ways in which he can get 8?

(b) How can he get 7?

(c) How can he get 2?

④ Allan Stewart wanted to change his car. The list price of his new Ford was £12 000 but the salesman offered to give him a discount of 10% if he did not have to take Allan's old car in part exchange. If Allan did offer his car in part exchange the allowance would be £3500 but there would then be no discount.

Allan made further inquiries and found that a colleague would buy his car for £3000 cash.
What would you advise him to do – sell his car privately or part exchange it with the garage?

⑤ How many different parallelograms can be drawn on this 2 × 2 grid? One of them is drawn for you. Do not count squares and rectangles.

Now try to solve the same problem for a 3 × 3 grid.

⑥ Using all four of the digits 1, 2, 3, 4 once only, and the signs +, −, ×, ÷ as many times as you wish, show how you can make the numbers:

(a) 13   (b) 45   (c) 127   (d) 24.

⑦ Which two of these shapes will fit together to make a cube?

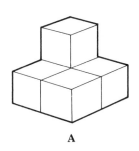
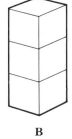
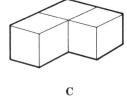

      A   **B**   **C**   **D**

⑧ (a) Verify that

$$2 = 1 \times 2$$
$$2 + 4 = 2 \times 3$$
$$2 + 4 + 6 = 3 \times 4$$
$$\text{and} \qquad 2 + 4 + 6 + 8 = 4 \times 5$$

(b) Use this pattern to find
  (i) the sum of the first 5 even numbers
  (ii) the sum of the first 20 even numbers

(c) How many consecutive even numbers, starting at 2, have a total of   (i) 56   (ii) 930?

103

(9) (a) How many centimetres are there in a metre?

(b) How many metres are there in a kilometre?

(c) On a map 1 cm represents 1 km.

   (i) What is the actual length, in kilometres, represented by 12 cm on the map?

   (ii) What is the scale of the map?

(10) Tony and Rena want to go to stay at the Nona Hotel in Majorca sometime next summer. The prices per person for the various dates of departure are given in the table.

Board Arrangement: Half-board

Number of nights	7	10	11	14
1 May – 7 May	217	243	253	285
8 May – 14 May	225	253	263	295
15 May – 21 May	235	262	272	305
22 May – 27 May	267	283	293	327
28 May – 13 June	254	286	296	330
14 June – 27 June	257	298	308	342
28 June – 11 July	267	305	315	352
12 July – 18 July	280	320	330	367
19 July – 25 July	288	335	345	382
26 July – 8 Aug	284	333	343	379
9 Aug – 19 Aug	287	332	342	377
20 Aug – 6 Sep	292	325	335	371
7 Sep – 13 Sep	277	318	328	363
14 Sep – 20 Sep	247	277	287	321
21 Sep – 3 Oct	239	266	276	310
4 Oct – 17 Oct	232	257	267	300
18 Oct – 24 Oct	222	–	–	–

DEPARTURES ON OR BETWEEN

Supplements per person per night: Full-board £2.25

(a) How much will it cost them for 11 nights half-board if they leave on

   (i) 3 June   (ii) 14 September?

(b) How much will 14 nights half-board cost them if they leave on

   (i) 19 July   (ii) 16 August?

(c) How much will 14 nights full-board cost them if they leave on
 (i) 18 July (ii) 16 October?

(d) Which is cheaper: 7 nights full-board leaving on 10 August or 11
 nights half-board leaving on 10 May?

(e) They have £700 between them to spend on board arrangements
 and they want a 14 night holiday with full-board. Between which
 dates must they travel?

(f) How much more will it cost each of them for an 11-night full-
 board holiday leaving on 30 May, than a 7-night half-board
 holiday leaving on 20 June?

Exercise 40

(1) The cash price of a music centre is £575. It can be bought on credit
 terms by paying a deposit of 20% of the cash price and 36 monthly
 payments of £17.90.

(a) How much is the deposit?
(b) What is the total of the 36 monthly payments?
(c) How much is the total credit price?
(d) How much is saved by paying cash?

(2) When Kim gets up at 7.30 a.m. she always winds her watch. It takes
 $2\frac{1}{2}$ turns for the watch to become fully wound. When she winds it at
 night before going to bed the same job takes her 5 turns. At what
 time does she go to bed?

(3)

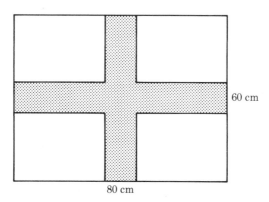

80 cm

The sketch shows the red cross of St George on a white background.
The flag measures 80 cm by 60 cm. If the area of red is arranged to be
equal to the area of white how wide is the cross?

105

(4) How many different four-digit numbers can you make from the digits 1, 2, 3 and 4 if all four digits are to be used exactly once in each number? What is the difference between the largest number you can make and the smallest number?
Without writing down all the possible numbers, can you say what the total of all these numbers will be? Give a reason for your answer.

(5)

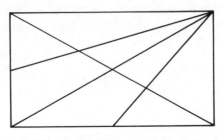

How many triangles can you see in this figure?

(6) Thirty teams enter a knock-out competition. How many rounds are necessary to find the winner? How many teams will get a bye (that is they will not need to play) in the first round? How many matches will be played altogether if there is a winner in every match?

(7)

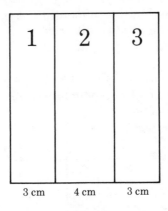

'A Companion to Bee Keeping' is in three volumes. Volume 1 is 3 cm thick, volume 2 is 4 cm thick and volume 3 is 3 cm thick. All three books have glossy hard covers 2 mm thick. They stand together on a bookshelf in the normal way.

(a) What is the thickness of Volume 1 excluding the covers?
(b) Volume 2 has 360 leaves (not pages!). What is the thickness of each leaf?
(c) How many leaves are there in Volume 3?
(d) How far is it from the last page of Volume 1 to the first page of Volume 2?
(e) How far is it from the first page of Volume 1 to the last page of Volume 3?

8 If $254 \times 63 = 16\,002$, find, without using a calculator,

(a) $\dfrac{16\,002}{254}$

(d) $160.02 \div 2.54$

(b) 2.54×6.3

(e) 0.254×0.63.

(c) $16.002 \div 0.63$

(f) $\dfrac{160\,020}{6300}$

9 When Diana leaves Bishton she has a choice of routes to go to Wickham. These are shown on the sketch which also gives the distances in kilometres between the various towns.

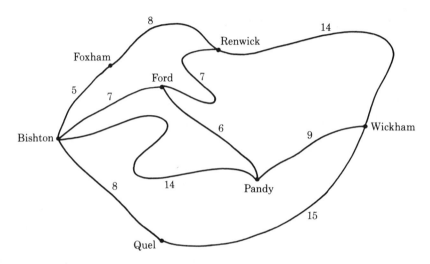

(a) How many different routes are there?
(b) What is the distance from Bishton to Wickham using each acceptable route?
(c) Which route is the shortest?
(d) Is it possible for a commercial traveller to leave his office in Pandy, visit all the other towns and return to his office without travelling along any road twice?
If it is possible, how long is the journey?

10 Jonathan collects four-digit car numbers. One day last week he saw just three of them. When he had written them down he noticed that:

(a) the first number consisted of four consecutive digits in the correct order
(b) the second number consisted of the same four digits but in reverse order
(c) the third number was formed from the same four digits but they were mixed up.
When he added the three car numbers together the total was 21 300. Can you deduce what the three car numbers were?

Exercise 41

① Change each of the following decimals into a fraction in its lowest terms:

(a) 0.3   (b) 0.8   (c) 0.75   (d) 0.6.

② Sandra calculates her wages by using the formula

$$\text{Wage} = \text{number of hours} \times \text{rate per hour}$$

(a) Use this formula to find Sandra's wage if:
   (i) she works 35 hours at £4 per hour
   (ii) she works 40 hours at £4.80 per hour
   (iii) she works 39 hours at £5.35 per hour.
(b) Use the same formula to find Sandra's hourly rate if she gets £183.60 for working 36 hours.
(c) How many hours does Sandra work if she earns £247 when the hourly rate is £6.50?

③ Mario has a 5 p, a 7 p and a 9 p stamp. In how many different ways can he stick these three stamps in a row on an envelope?

④ Edmund and Lancing start out together from base camp in an attempt to conquer a mountain peak. Each of them can carry sufficient supplies to last 16 days. No additional supplies are available along the route. If it takes Lancing 12 days to scale the peak and the same length of time to return to the base camp, determine whether or not they have adequate supplies for both climbers to return to base camp without running short. Supplies can be stored on the outward journey for use on the return journey.

⑤ The president of the local rugby club is always elected, or re-elected, at the Annual General Meeting held on 1 March each year. Given below is a list of the presidents so far this century.

1900–02	S. Green
1902–05	A. A. Douglas
1905–08	T. Fowler
1908–22	S. Green
1922–28	P. Cave
1928–37	D. S. Short
1937–54	P. Baldrick
1954–62	H. Anthony
1962–76	D. S. Short
1976–79	W. May
1979–	O. D. Williams

(a) For how many years was A. A. Douglas president?

(b) Who was president for the greatest number of years without a break? How long was this?

(c) Who was president for the greatest number of years? How long was this?

(d) Assuming that O. D. Williams continues with unbroken service, on what date will he be elected to begin his 25th year?

(6) Use the formula:

$$\text{Area of triangle} = \tfrac{1}{2} \text{ base} \times \text{perpendicular height}$$

to find the area of each of the shaded regions given below.

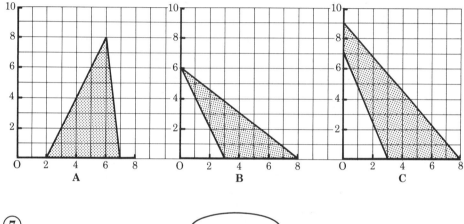

A B C

(7)

Which jar gives the best value for money?

(8) The Canine Society, the Young Farmers' Club and the Camera Club hold regular meetings in the civic centre. The Canine Society meets every fifth day, the Young Farmers' Club meets every seventh day and the Camera Club meets every thirteenth day. In 1991 all three groups met on 1 January. Mr Wellbeloved wanted to visit all three on the same day but was unable to make it on 1 January. How long did he have to wait until all three groups were due to meet again on the same day?

109

⑨ This graph illustrates the results obtained by measuring the heights of 80 first-year pupils. It shows the total number of pupils below a certain height, e.g. there are 16 pupils shorter than 140 cm.

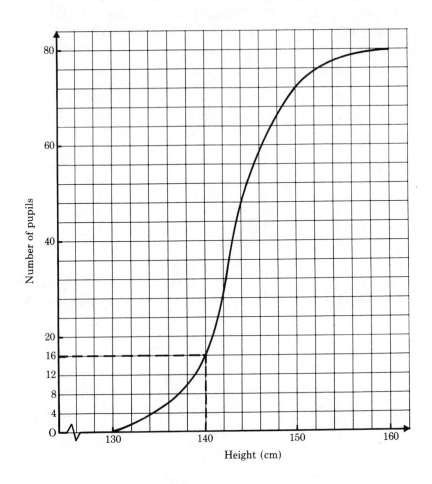

(a) How many first-year pupils are shorter than
    (i) 150 cm   (ii) 144 cm   (iii) 136 cm?

(b) Use your answers to part (a) to find:
    (i) the number of pupils that are taller than 150 cm
    (ii) the number of pupils whose heights are between 144 cm and 150 cm.
    (Assume that there is no pupil whose height is exactly either 144 cm or 150 cm.)

(c) Estimate the height of the fortieth pupil if they all stand in a line arranged in order of height from shortest to tallest.

(10) Jim shows Kathy 27 coins. He tells her that 26 of them are of equal weight but that one is slightly lighter than the others. She has a simple balance on which she can place some in one scale pan and weigh them against others in the other scale pan. If she can find the lighter coin by making no more than three weighings she can keep the lot. Can you advise her?

Exercise 42

(1) Name each of the shapes given below and for each one state:
   (a) the number of axes of symmetry it has
   (b) its order of rotational symmetry.

(2) A store sells tapes at £5 and £7. Wasim buys some of each and pays £67 for them. How many of each does he buy?

(3) A second-hand car salesman sold two cars for £4800 each. On the first he made a 50% profit while on the second he made a 25% loss. Did he make a profit or a loss on the combined sales?

111

Arrange these three shapes to give a quadrilateral that has exactly two axes of symmetry. The shapes can be turned over or round. What name do you give to this shape? Does your shape have rotational symmetry?

⑤

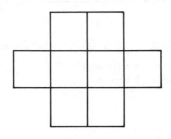

(a) How many squares can you see in this figure?
(b) How many rectangles, other than squares, are there?

⑥ Donna travels from home to work and back again five days a week. A peak hour return costs £3.30. A 13-week season ticket costs £166.60.

(a) How much does Donna save if she buys a 13-week season ticket in preference to a peak hour return ticket each day?
(b) In one 13-week period, for which Donna had bought a season ticket she was on sick leave for four days and took a two-week holiday. With hindsight would it have been cheaper to have bought peak hour daily returns?

⑦ A sheet of A0 paper has an area of approximately 1 square metre and measures 841 mm by 1189 mm. An A0 sheet gives two A1 sheets when its shorter edges are folded together and the sheet cut along the fold. In a similar way an A1 sheet gives two A2 sheets, and so on for all the other paper sizes as far as A8. Any length that is not exact is rounded down.

(a) Find the dimensions of each sheet size from A1 to A8. Give each dimension in millimetres.
(b) Write down the approximate area of (i) an A4 sheet, (ii) an A6 sheet, as a fraction of a square metre. (You do not need to know the dimensions of the sheet to work this out.)

⑧ Complete each diagram so that the number in any square is equal to the sum of the numbers in the two circles on opposite sides of that square.

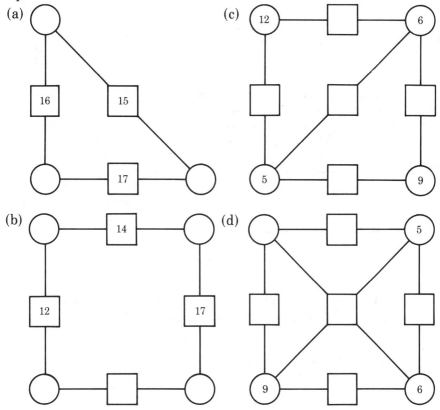

(a)

(c)

(b)

(d)

⑨ The alphabet used by blind people is called Braille. It is named after Louis Braille, a Frenchman. Dots are put in one or more of six different positions on a 3 × 2 rectangle. For example, there are six different ways in which five dots can be put on the rectangle. These are shown below.

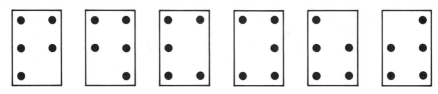

In how many different ways:

(a) can one dot be put on the rectangle
(b) can two dots be put on the rectangle
(c) can three dots be put on the rectangle
(d) can four dots be put on the rectangle
(e) can six dots be put on the rectangle?

113

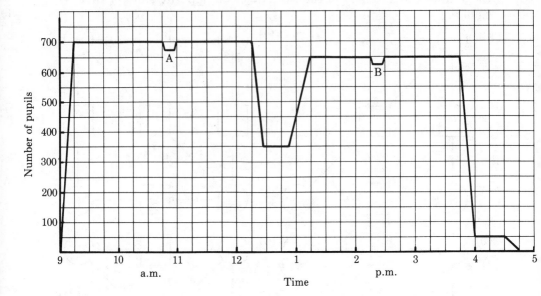

The graph shows the number of pupils on the premises at Staverly School one day last term. Use the graph to answer the following questions.

(a) What time do you think school starts:
 (i) in the morning
 (ii) in the afternoon?

(b) Can you explain what is probably happening at the two points on the graph marked A and B?

(c) Explain what is happening at the end of the school day.

(d) What percentage of the pupils who were present in the morning left the premises at lunchtime?

(e) On the morning in question $\frac{1}{8}$ of all the pupils on the register were absent. What fraction were present?
How many pupils were there on the register?
How many pupils were absent in the afternoon?

⑪ An oil tanker has an iron ladder with 55 rungs, each 30 cm apart, fixed to its side. The tanker is at anchor in port and at noon the level of the tide is such that 40 rungs are visible above the water line. If the level of the tide rises at a rate of 30 cm per hour, how many rungs are visible above the water line at 6 p.m. that evening?

114

Exercise 43

①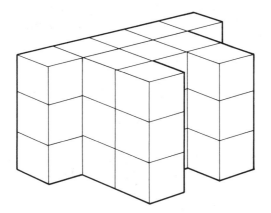

(a) How many small cubes are needed to make this stack?
(b) What is the least number of extra cubes needed to build this
stack into a cube without dismantling the original stack?

② In a particular year Christmas day falls on a Friday. On which day of
the week are the following dates that year:

(a) Boxing Day
(b) New Year's Eve
(c) 18 December?
(d) 10 December
(e) 1 December

③ (a) Teresa has a cube of edge 1 cm while Dean has a cube of edge
  2 cm. For each cube write down:
    (i) the total length of all the edges
    (ii) the total surface area
    (iii) the volume.
(b) Sean has a cube with a surface area of 96 cm^2.
    (i) What is the length of an edge of this cube?
    (ii) What is the volume of this cube?
(c) Ross has a cube with a volume of 27 cm^3.
    (i) What is the length of an edge of Ross's cube?
    (ii) Find its total surface area.

④ I have two coins with a total value of 30 p. One of them is *not* a 20 p
coin. What is the value of the other?

(5) An international company has offices in London, New York and Tokyo.
The London office is open from 9.30 a.m. to 4.30 p.m.
The New York office is open from 2.30 p.m. to 8.30 p.m.
The Tokyo office is open from 1.00 a.m. to 6.30 a.m.
(All these times are given in London time.)

(a) For how long are the London and New York offices both open at the same time?
(b) Is there any part of the day when all three offices are open?
(c) How many hours are there in a day when all three offices are closed?

(6) Use long division to find, to at least nine decimal places, the decimal values of all the fractions from $\frac{1}{13}$ to $\frac{12}{13}$ that have 13 as the denominator.
Are any of your answers recurring decimals? How many digits are there in each cycle? How many cycles of digits are identical, though starting at different places in the cycle?

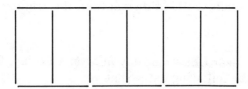

In a market 13 hurdles have been used to make 6 identical sheep pens. Unfortunately one of the hurdles gets broken. How is it possible to arrange the 12 remaining hurdles and still have 6 identical sheep pens?
Show that the ground area that each sheep has is reduced by about 13%.

(8) Tim found an old family album while clearing out the attic. It contained the following information:
Thomas Lee Curzon born 3 March 1858 died 4 June 1947
Sandra Jane Curzon (formerly Smith) born 21 Nov. 1865 died 16 Feb. 1924
Their children:
Lee Roy born 5 Nov. 1884 died 23 Dec. 1936
Catharine Amanda born 7 Jan. 1886 died 4 May 1959
Jonathan Fredrick born 23 May 1887 died 16 June 1962
Mary Ann born 15 Oct. 1890 died 1 March 1895

(a) How old was Thomas when he died?
(b) How old was Sandra when she died?
(c) Which child had the longest life?
(d) Which child had the shortest life?
(e) How old was Thomas when Mary Anne died?

116

(f) How old was Catharine when her mother died?
(g) How old was Mary when her father died?
(h) How old was Jonathan when Catharine had her tenth birthday?

⑨ The digits 1 to 6 are to be written in order and one multiplication sign is to be placed somewhere in-between them. Between which two digits must it be placed to give the largest product?

⑩ The least number of straight lines that can be drawn on a flat surface to enclose an area is three. Three straight lines give a triangle. *In the shapes referred to below*, which are drawn on dotted paper with the dots arranged in squares, *no dot must appear within a shape*. If three dots are joined we have a triangle. If four dots are joined we can have a square or a parallelogram or a triangle.
For example

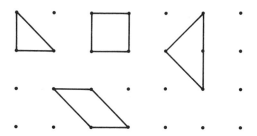

The area enclosed when three points are joined, provided that they are not all in a straight line, is $\frac{1}{2}$ a square unit. When four points are joined the area is 1 square unit.

(a) On dotted paper draw as many different shapes as you can joining five points. What is the area of each shape?
(b) Repeat part (a) using: (i) six points (ii) seven points.
(c) Copy and complete this table which connects the number of points (p) with the area enclosed (A).

Number of points (p)	3	4	5	6	7	10	20
Area enclosed in square units (A)	$\frac{1}{2}$	1					

 ⑪

A closed wooden rectangular box has external measurements 43 cm × 35 cm × 18 cm. It is made from wood $1\frac{1}{2}$ cm thick. Find the capacity of the box.

Exercise 44

(1) A recipe for 10 small cakes uses 70 g fat, 70 g castor sugar, 100 g flour and 2 eggs.

(a) How much castor sugar is needed to make 25 of these cakes?

(b) How many eggs are needed to make 35 of these cakes?

(c) I have 150 g flour. How many cakes can I make?

(2) There were three candidates for the position of Head Girl at Stannah School. The fifth-form votes were: Eschle 64, Dennison 83, Wozencroft 16. There were six spoilt papers and seven pupils failed to vote.

(a) Who was appointed Head Girl and by how many votes?

(b) How many fifth formers voted?

(c) How many fifth formers were eligible to vote?

(3) The postage on a parcel is 71 p. Can Eddie put the correct postage on this parcel if he has only 4 p and 9 p stamps?

(4) The sum of the scores on the opposite faces of a fair dice is 7.

(a) How many spots are there on the face opposite to the 2?

(b) How many spots are there altogether on a dice?

(c) Which of these nets could be used to make this dice:

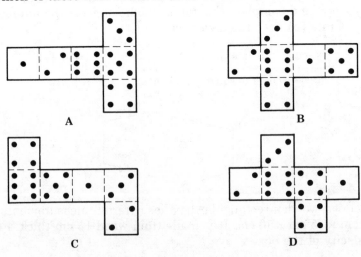

A   B

C   D

118

⑤ A small mammal doubled its weight every day for the first five days of its life. It weighed 480 g when it was four days old.
  (a) What was its weight when:
    (i) it was five days old
    (ii) it was three days old?
  (b) Find its birth weight.

⑥ A factory employs 350 workers. Each worker is paid £200 per week. If the work force is reduced by 10% but those that remain receive a 10% increase in their wages, will the total wage bill for the factory be more or less than it was originally?

⑦ Anne, Bill, Colin and Diana share a £50 prize. Bill gets £1 more than Anne, Colin gets £1 more than Bill and Diana gets £1 more than Colin. How much does each get?

⑧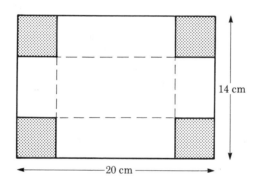

Four equal squares (which are shaded) of side 4 cm are removed from the corners of a rectangular piece of card measuring 20 cm by 14 cm. The card is then folded about the dotted lines to make an open box.
  (a) How deep is the box?
  (b) Find the length and breadth of the base of the box.
  (c) What area of card is wasted?
  (d) What is the capacity of the box?
  (e) How many solid cubes of side 2 cm can be fitted into this box?

⑨ It takes six men eight days to build a wall.
  (a) How long would it take four men to build the same wall, assuming that they all work at the same rate?
  (b) If each man works half as long again each day, how long would it take four men to build this wall?

(10) The factors of 10 are 1, 2, 5 and 10. If we ignore 10 and add up the other factors, we get $1 + 2 + 5 = 8$. 1, 2 and 5 are called the Aliquot factors of 10.

Now do the same for 8. The factors of 8 are 1, 2, 4 and 8 so the sum of the Aliquot factors is 7.

The factors of 7 are 1 and 7 so the Aliquot factor of 7 is 1.

We can set these out in a chain,

i.e. $$10 \to 8 \to 7 \to 1,$$

where the arrow means 'the sum of the factors of the number other than itself'.

Similarly

$$15 \to 9 \to 4 \to 3 \to 1.$$

(a) Write down the chains for:
  (i) 12 (ii) 20 (iii) 30 (iv) 36.

(b) Write down the chains for
  (i) 48 (ii) 11 (iii) 31 (iv) 6.

(c) The sum of the Aliquot factors of 496 is very interesting! Find it.

(d) Find the sum of the Aliquot factors for 1210 and repeat this for the answer you get.

Exercise 45

(1) A coach company charges passengers 8 p per mile for a single journey and 7 p per mile for a return journey. The distance from Manchester to Dover is 265 miles.

(a) How much is a single ticket from Manchester to Dover?

(b) How much is saved by buying a return ticket rather than two single tickets for the return journey from Manchester to Dover?

(2) (a) Which would you prefer, a tonne of 2 p coins or a tonne of 1 p coins?

(b) Which would you prefer, a tonne of 50 p coins or a tonne of £1 coins?

(3) A music shop sells compact discs at £7 and £11. Mandy buys some of each and pays £43. How many of each does she buy?

(4) Jeff makes concrete by mixing cement, sand and gravel by volume in the ratio 1:2:5.

(a) How much sand would he mix with $0.4 \, \text{m}^3$ of cement?

(b) How much gravel would he mix with $0.5 \, \text{m}^3$ of cement?

(c) How much sand would be needed to make $24 \, \text{m}^3$ of concrete?

⑤

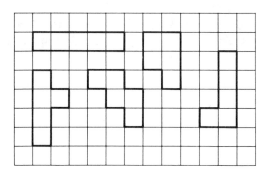

Can you fit these five shapes (they are called pentominoes) together to form a square?

⑥

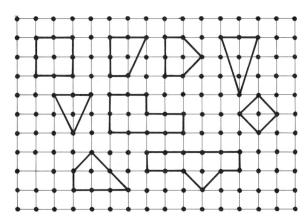

(a) In this diagram, each polygon surrounds one grid intersection that is marked with a dot. Draw some more polygons that surround one dot.

(b) Find a rule connecting the area of each shape, i.e. the number of small squares within its boundary, with the number of dots on its boundary.

(c) What is the area of a polygon with one dot inside and 12 dots on its boundary?

(d) How many dots are there on the boundary of a polygon with an area of seven squares if there is one dot inside?

⑦ Solve this cross-fraction puzzle.

$a = \frac{1}{2} + \frac{1}{2}$ $b = \frac{1}{4} + \frac{1}{4}$

$c = \frac{3}{4} - \frac{1}{2}$ $d = b + c$

121

⑧ I expect to get 30 000 miles out of the set of four tyres on my car. Each tyre costs £90. How much per mile do I spend on tyres?

⑨ (a)

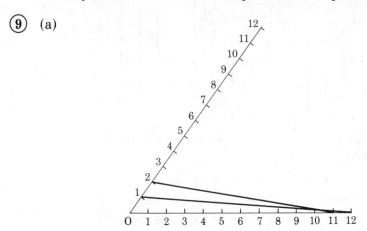

Draw two straight lines from a point O enclosing an acute angle of your own choice. Along each line mark 12 points at one centimetre intervals and number them from 1 to 12. Join the points, one on each line such that the sum of the two numbers is always 13. (Two of these lines are shown in the diagram.) These lines give the outline for a 'curve'. Draw the curve freehand as well as you can.

(b) Repeat this exercise when the two given lines are drawn at right angles to each other.

⑩ A square board is divided into small squares of different types.
There are: corner squares, denoted by C,
diagonal squares, denoted by D,
inner squares, denoted by I
and squares on the edge, other than corner squares, denoted by E.

Some squares belong to more than one type, for example, a corner square is also a diagonal square, while some inner squares are also diagonal squares. The different types of squares for a 5 × 5 board are shown below.

C D	E	E	E	C D
E	D I	I	D I	E
E	I	D I	I	E
E	D I	I	D I	E
D C	E	E	E	D C

122

(a) Copy and complete the following table.

Board size	Number of squares on board	Type of square				Number of squares belonging to two types
		C	D	I	E	
3×3						
4×4						
5×5	25	4	9	9	12	
6×6						
7×7						
8×8						

(b) A board has 10×10 squares. How many diagonal squares does it have? How many inner squares are there?

(c) A board measures 15×15. How many diagonal squares are there? How many edge squares are there?

(d) A board has 144 inner squares. What is the size of the board? How many edge squares will it have?

Exercise 46

(1) Which is the better pay and by how much:
(a) £258 per week
(b) £1166 per calendar month, or
(c) £13 500 per annum?

(2) (a) Work out:
(i) $4^2 + 4 + 5$ (ii) $6^2 + 6 + 7$ (iii) $9^2 + 9 + 10$.
(b) Use your results from (a) to write down the value of:
(i) $27^2 + 27 + 28$ (ii) $53^2 + 53 + 54$.

(3) The speedometer on my car reads 10% more than the actual speed of the car.
(a) When I am travelling at 60 m.p.h. what speed is my speedometer showing?
(b) When the speedometer shows 77 m.p.h. how fast am I travelling?

(4) The left-hand digits are a reflection of the right-hand digits when my digital watch shows the time 12:51. State nine other times at which this happens.

(5) A coach leaves Liverpool at 10.43 to travel to London. The journey is scheduled to take 4 hours 35 minutes but actually takes 12 minutes longer than this. At what time does the coach arrive in London?

⑥

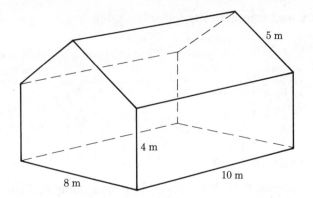

The sketch shows a workshop with a rectangular base measuring 10 m by 8 m. The pitched roof has two sloping rectangular faces each measuring 5 m by 10 m. What volume of water, in cubic metres, falls on this workshop during a storm when the rainfall is 10 millimetres?

⑦

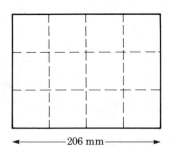

206 mm

A rectangular piece of wood is 206 mm long. It is to be sawn into 12 identical square pieces. If each saw cut is 2 mm wide find:

(a) the length of the side of one of the 12 square pieces.
(b) the width of the original rectangle.

⑧ What do the angles at a point add up to?

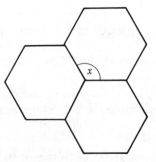

Three hexagonal paving stones fit together as shown. What is the size of the angle marked x?

A builder lays red and cream hexagonal paving stones in such a way that each red slab is completely surrounded by cream slabs.

(a) How many cream slabs are needed to surround one red slab?

(b) How many extra cream slabs are needed when another red slab is added to the pattern referred to in part (a)?

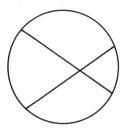

(a) Draw a circle with a radius of about 5 cm, together with two chords. Each chord is divided into two parts. Each part is called a line segment. How many line segments are there when there are two chords?

(b) Draw another chord that does not pass through the point of intersection of the first two chords. How many line segments are there in total now?

(c) Draw a fourth chord such that no three chords intersect at the same point. How many line segments are there altogether now? Copy and complete this table without drawing any more chords.

Number of chords	Number of line segments
1	1
2	
3	
4	
5	
6	
7	
8	
9	
10	

(d) How many line segments are there if there are 25 chords?

(e) If there are 400 line segments how many chords are there?

⑩ A prime number is a number that can be divided exactly only by itself and 1. The first eight prime numbers are 2, 3, 5, 7, 11, 13, 17, 19. Several people over the years have found interesting facts about prime numbers.

(a) Goldbach found that:
   every even number greater than 4 is the sum of two primes,
   for example, $6 = 3 + 3$, $8 = 3 + 5$, $10 = 3 + 7$.
   How could you write (i) 120   (ii) 154, as the sum of two primes?

(b) Goldbach also found that every odd number greater than 7 is the sum of three primes,

e.g. $9 = 3 + 3 + 3, 11 = 3 + 3 + 5, 13 = 3 + 5 + 5$.

How could you write (i) 151   (ii) 119 as the sum of three primes?

(c) Primes are said to be twins if they are consecutive odd numbers, e.g. 17 and 19. List all the twin primes less than 100.

(d) 17, 19 and 23 are triple primes, that is they differ respectively by 2 and 4. List all the triple primes less than 100.

(e) How many primes are there:
  (i) less than 50
  (ii) less than 100 but greater than 50
  (iii) less than 150 but greater than 100
  (iv) less than 200 but greater than 150?

Exercise 47

① 75 $= 37 + 38$, i.e. 75 can be written as the sum of two consecutive whole numbers.

(a) Can you write 75 as the sum of
  (i) three consecutive whole numbers
  (ii) four consecutive whole numbers
  (iii) five consecutive whole numbers
  (iv) six consecutive whole numbers?

(b) Are there any other lists of consecutive whole numbers that give a total of 75?

② (a)

Wally places 7 cubes in a row on the table. How many square faces of these cubes are exposed? How many are hidden?

(b) Tina builds the same cubes into a stack. How many square faces are exposed now?

(3) A book with 320 pages is 16 millimetres thick excluding the covers. How thick, in millimetres, is the paper on which this book is printed?

(4) A league has eight clubs which play fixtures each Saturday. The results for the first four weeks of the season are given below. The home team is given first and the score is written for the home side so that A–B 2–1 means that team A were at home and won 2–1.

Week				
1	A–B 2–1	C–D 1–3	E–F 5–2	G–H 2–0
2	A–C 3–0	B–D 2–2	E–H 0–1	F–G 1–1
3	C–B 1–1	F–A 0–0	D–H 3–3	G–E 3–1
4	C–E 2–1	B–E 3–1	D–G 1–2	H–A 0–2

The points awarded are: 3 for a win, 1 for a draw, 0 for a loss.

(a) Work out the positions of the eight clubs in the league table after four weeks.

(b) It is proposed that the league introduces a new system of awarding points, namely:

Away win	4 points
Home win	3 points
Score draw	2 points
No-score draw	1 point
Loss	0 points

Work out the positions of the eight clubs after four weeks if the new system had been introduced.

(5) (a) If we divide a number a by one more than itself the answer is $\frac{1}{4}$. Find a.

(b) If we divide a number b by one more than itself the answer is $\frac{3}{7}$. Find b.

(c) What is the product of a and b?

(6) How many positive whole numbers are there between 100 and 10 000 that use the digits 2, 3 and 4 together in the correct order?

(7) There is an even number of houses in Hartley Street. Starting from one end the odd numbers are along one side and the even numbers are along the other side. Number 1 is thus opposite number 2. Pete lives in number 121. If the numbering had started at the opposite end Pete would be living in number 43. How many houses are there in the street?

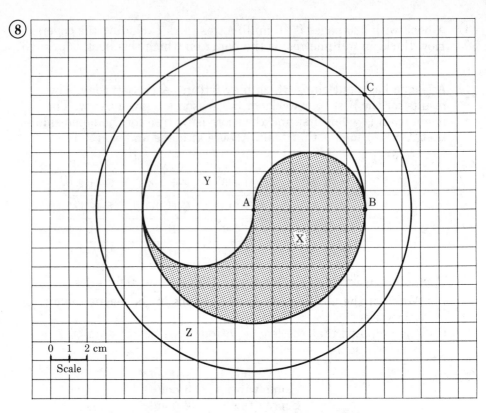

⑧

The diagram shows Yin and Yan, the old Chinese symbols, enclosed within a circle. Draw this shape *full size* on squared paper.

Write down the lengths of AB and BC and use them to calculate the length of AC. Hence find the area of:

(a) X (b) Y (c) the large circle (d) the small circle (e) Z.

What can you say about the areas X, Y and Z?

⑨ A rectangular piece of card measuring 12 cm by 9 cm is to be used to make a small open rectangular box. The diagram, which is drawn half-size, shows one way of doing this.

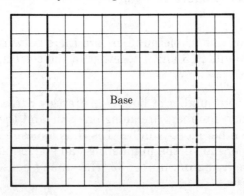

Base

(a) How many different boxes can be made from this piece of card if the length and breadth of the base is to be a whole number of centimetres? Draw each possibility on squared paper.

(b) For each different box find
  (i) its dimensions
  (ii) its total external surface area
  (iii) its capacity.

(c) Use the information you have found in (b) to state whether each of these statements is true (T) or false (F).
  A The box with the largest base has the greatest capacity.
  B The box with the smallest total external surface area has the smallest capacity.
  C The box with the greatest capacity is as deep as it is wide.

(d) Find the dimensions of the largest *cubical* open box that can be made from a rectangular card measuring 12 cm by 9 cm. How much card is wasted?

⑩ (a)

The sum of	First number in the group			
	1	2	3	4
2 consecutive whole numbers	3	5	7	
3 consecutive whole numbers	6	9		
4 consecutive whole numbers	10			
5 consecutive whole numbers				
6 consecutive whole numbers				

Copy and complete this table.
The numbers in the first line result from adding the consecutive whole numbers two at a time, e.g. if the first number is 3 we add 3 + 4 and get 7 which is the entry beneath 3. In the second line of the table we add three consecutive whole numbers, e.g. if the first number is 2 we add 2 + 3 + 4, i.e. 9, so 9 goes beneath 2 in the second line of the table.

(b) Can you see number patterns in the table?
Write down the next five numbers in each row simply by using the pattern for that row.

(c) Write down the next row of the table.

(d) Which numbers between 1 and 50 cannot be written as the sum of consecutive whole numbers?

⑪ A certain type of cell can reproduce itself every minute. When one such cell is placed inside a small container it takes exactly one hour before there are enough cells to fill the container completely. If two cells had been placed in the container at the start how long would it have taken to produce sufficient cells to fill it?

Exercise 48

(1) A pen and a pencil cost 60 p. If a pen costs 24 p more than a pencil how much does a pencil cost?

(2) The season of Spring starts on 21 March and ends on 20 June. How many days is this?

(3) Find the smallest positive whole number which when divided by 7 gives a remainder of 3 and when divided by 9 also gives a remainder of 3.

(4) Find the value of:

(a) $\dfrac{1 + \frac{2}{3}}{\frac{2}{3}}$
(b) $\dfrac{1}{1 - \frac{2}{3}}$
(c) $\dfrac{1}{1 \div \frac{2}{3}}$
(d) $\dfrac{2 \times \frac{2}{3}}{1 - \frac{1}{3}}$.

(5) The rules for producing a certain number chain starting with a two-figure number are:

> Add the number of tens to the square of the number of units. Stop the chain when you get a single figure.

For example:

$$73 \to 7 + 3^2 = 7 + 9 = 16 \to 1 + 36 = 37 \to 3 + 49 = 52 \to 5 + 4 = 9.$$

Apply these instructions to the numbers:

(a) 42 (b) 53 (c) 85.

(6)

Pieces of London silver are always marked with a date letter. The letters of the alphabet, excluding J, V, W, X, Y and Z, are used in order as date letters. This gives a 20-year cycle. The century years, for example 1800, are given the letter E.
In the 19th century what are the possible dates if the letter is

(a) E (b) M (c) T?

(7) A goods train, 500 metres long, is travelling at a constant 30 kilometres per hour and enters a tunnel $1\frac{1}{2}$ kilometres long. How long is it before the rear of the train emerges from the tunnel?

⑧

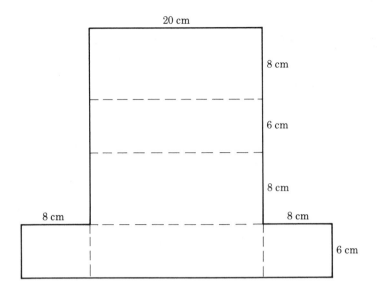

20 cm

8 cm

6 cm

8 cm

8 cm   8 cm

6 cm

8 cm

This is a net for a box with a lid.

(a) What are the dimensions of
    (i) its base   (ii) its long sides   (iii) its lid?
(b) What area of card is needed to make this box?
(c) What is the capacity of the box?

⑨ The houses in Coronation Street are numbered in order from one end. The odd numbers are on one side of the street and the even numbers are on the other. My house is number 47. If the numbering had started at the other end of the street my house would have been number 29. How many houses are there on my side of Coronation Street?

⑩ How many consecutive zeros are there at the end of the number that is produced when:

(a) all the whole numbers from 1 to 10 inclusive are multiplied together
(b) all the whole numbers from 1 to 30 inclusive are multiplied together
(c) all the whole numbers from 1 to 50 inclusive are multiplied together
(d) all the whole numbers from 1 to 100 inclusive are multiplied together
(e) all the whole numbers from 10 to 50 inclusive are multiplied together?

(Note: You do not need to multiply all the numbers together to obtain each answer.)

Exercise 49

(1) If 1 oz = 28 g, change:
  (a) 4 oz into grams
  (b) 20 oz into grams
  (c) 280 g into ounces
  (d) 182 g into ounces.

(2) The cooking time for roasting beef is given as 30 minutes per pound plus 25 minutes extra. At what time should Jean-Paul put a $5\frac{1}{2}$ lb joint of beef in the oven if it is to be ready by 1 p.m.?

(3) (a) In how many different ways can Eric make each of these scores with one dart:
  (i) 12   (ii) 13   (iii) 14?
  (b) In how many different ways can Esther make each of these scores with two darts if both darts score:
  (i) 120   (ii) 5   (iii) 13?

(4) If ten is five less than one too many, how many is enough?

(5) Last year the first day of Summer was 21 June and the last day of Summer was 23 September. How many Summer days were there?

(6) The table shows the monthly repayments in pounds on a bank loan ranging from £500 to £10 000, over a period of between 1 and 3 years, at both 10% p.a. and 15% p.a.

Amount of loan (£)		500		1000		2000		5000		10 000	
Interest rate (%)		10	15	10	15	10	15	10	15	10	15
Length of	12	45.85	47.90	91.70	95.80	183.40	191.60	458.50	479	917	958
repayment	24	25.20	27.55	50.40	55.10	100.80	110.20	252	275.50	504	551
term in months	36	18.55	21.10	37.10	42.20	74.20	84.40	185.50	211	371	422

(a) What would be the total repayment on a bank loan of:
  (i) £1000 at 10% over 12 months
  (ii) £5000 at 15% over 24 months
  (iii) £2000 at 10% over 36 months
  (iv) £3000 at 15% over 24 months
  (v) £10 500 at 10% over 36 months.
(b) Marie wants to buy a new car and needs to borrow £5000. How much would she save by repaying the loan over 12 months rather than 36 months if the interest rate throughout the term of the loan is 15%?

(7) (a) If you are asked to write down the next two terms in the sequence 1, 3, 5, 7, 9, . . . you can probably do so quite easily since the numbers go up by 2 each time. The next two numbers are therefore 11 and 13.
  However, if you have to write down the next two numbers in the sequence 1, 3, 11, 25, 45, . . . the answer is not as obvious. Try it.

Look at this table

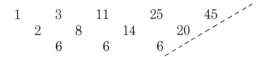

$$1 \quad 3 \quad 11 \quad 25 \quad 45$$
$$2 \quad 8 \quad 14 \quad 20$$

Can you see where the numbers in the second line come from?
They show the difference between each number and the next one.
Doing the same thing again the table becomes

$$1 \quad 3 \quad 11 \quad 25 \quad 45$$
$$2 \quad 8 \quad 14 \quad 20$$
$$6 \quad 6 \quad 6$$

Continuing the bottom line beyond the dashed line, we add more
6s. This means that we can fill in more numbers in the line
above, namely 20 + 6 or 26 and 26 + 6 or 32, and so on.
In the same way we can work back to the first line and fill in the
next two numbers, namely 45 + 26 or 71 and 71 + 32 or 103.
The table has thus become

$$1 \quad 3 \quad 11 \quad 25 \quad 45 \quad 71 \quad 103$$
$$2 \quad 8 \quad 14 \quad 20 \quad 26 \quad 32$$
$$6 \quad 6 \quad 6 \quad 6 \quad 6$$

The next two numbers in the given sequence are therefore 71 and
103. Can you find the two after that?

(b) Use the ideas you developed in part (a) to find the next two
numbers in each of these sequences:
(i) 1   3   10   22   39
(ii) 2   5   10   17   26
(iii) 3   4   11   24
(iv) 2   6   15   31   56
(v) 1   4   12   29.

⑧

Alun, Betty, Chris, Don and Elsie want to sit on five chairs that have
been set out in a row and numbered 1 to 5. They are to have a
photograph taken. Alun does not want to sit on chair number 1, Betty
does not want to sit on chair number 5, while Chris does not want to
sit at either end of the row. Betty wants to sit on a higher numbered
chair than Chris. Chris does not want to sit next to Betty and Elsie
does not want to sit next to Chris. Who sits where?

⑨

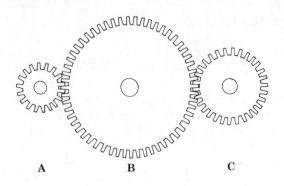

A B C

Three cog wheels mesh. Cog A has 20 teeth, cog B has 60 teeth and cog C has 30 teeth.

(a) The system starts by turning cog A clockwise.
 (i) How many turns will cog B make when cog A makes 12 turns?
 (ii) How many turns will cog C make when cog B makes 20 turns?
 (iii) How many turns will cog C make when cog A makes 30 turns?
(b) If cog C turns clockwise, in which direction will cog A turn?
(c) If cog B turns clockwise, in which direction will cog A turn?
(d) How many turns will cog A make when cog C makes 60 turns?

⑩ Bina's father is laying square tiles to form rectangles. Bina lays a string in a straight line from corner to corner each time her father lays two more tiles. All the rectangles are two tiles wide.

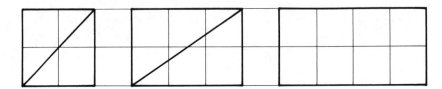

She makes a table to show how many tiles the string crosses for each rectangle

Number of tiles in width	Number of tiles in length	Number of tiles the string crosses
2	2	2
2	3	4
2	4	
2	5	
2	6	
2	7	
2	8	
2	9	
2	10	

(a) Copy and complete this table.
(b) How many tiles does the string cross when the rectangle is:
    (i) 2 tiles by 19 tiles   (ii) 2 tiles by 30 tiles?
(c) What happens if rectangles 3 tiles wide are considered?

Exercise 50

1. The sum of the numerator and denominator of a fraction is 19. If the numerator was 5 larger, the fraction would simplify to 1. What is the fraction?

2. Copy and complete the table given below. Add at least another six prime numbers of your own choice.

Prime number	Square of this prime number less 1	Answer to column 2 divided by 12
2		
3		
5		
7	$49 - 1 = 48$	
11		
13		

What do you notice about the numbers in the last column of the table?

3. In a 30 mile rally for vintage cars 30 cars used a total of 30 gallons of petrol. Assuming that the rate of consumption is unchanged how many gallons would 50 vintage cars use for a 50 mile rally?

4. Answer each question by making use of the additional information.
(a) Peter is listening to a symphony on a CD. What time should it finish?
Additional information:
    (i) The symphony lasts 40 minutes.
    (ii) It is one of Mozart's best known symphonies.
    (iii) He started listening to it at 7.30 p.m.
    (iv) It is about two-thirds of the way through at the moment.
(b) Alex is due to attend a meeting of the Photographic Society at 7 p.m. It will take him 20 minutes to walk there. Will he probably be late?
Additional information:
    (i) His car has broken down.
    (ii) His watch is 10 minutes fast.

(iii) He had finished his meal by 6.30 p.m.

(iv) It is 6.45 p.m. by his watch now.

(c) Jackie makes dresses for people who bring her the material. How much profit did she make last week?

Additional information:

(i) She charges £4.50 per hour.

(ii) She works about forty hours each week.

(iii) She never works on a Sunday.

(iv) Her expenses come to about £10 a week.

(v) She usually starts work at 9.30 a.m.

How many different triangles can be made by joining points on this grid? Sketch each one. Indicate which one has:

(a) the smallest area

(b) the largest area?

⑥ Take any whole number between 5 and 30. Now form a chain using these rules:

If the number is even find half of it.

If the number is odd, multiply it by 3 and add 1.

For example, if we start with 7 the chain is:

$$7 \to 22 \to 11 \to 34 \to 17 \to 52 \to 26 \to 13$$
$$\to 40 \to 20 \to 10 \to 5 \to 16 \to 8 \to 4 \to 2 \to 1$$

Form your own chains. What is the longest chain you can find? What is the shortest chain you can find?

⑦ Six boys went on holiday together. Five of them spent exactly £75 each but Ian was far more extravagant. He spent £50 more than the average for the party. How much did Ian spend?

⑧ Joan carried out a survey of the sixty pupils in her games group, to find out the number of brothers and sisters each pupil had. Her results are shown below.

1	2	0	2	3	1	2	2	1	0
0	1	2	1	2	1	1	3	1	2
2	1	6	1	0	2	1	1	3	1
1	0	2	1	0	0	2	0	0	1
0	4	1	0	4	1	0	1	1	1
2	2	3	0	1	2	1	3	1	3

Fill in the tally column in the table given below and hence fill in the frequency column

Number of brothers and sisters	Tally	Frequency
0		
1		
2		
3		
4		
5		
6		

(a) Which number of brothers and sisters occurred most frequently?

(b) Find the mean number of brothers and sisters for these sixty children.

(c) What is the most likely family size, excluding parents, for this group of children?

(d) What is the probability that if a pupil is chosen at random he/she:
   (i) has one brother or one sister
   (ii) belongs to one of four or more children?

⑨

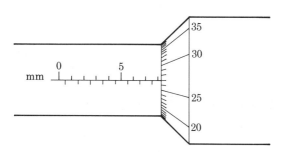

The reading on this micrometer is 8.27.
What is the reading on each of the following micrometers?

(a)

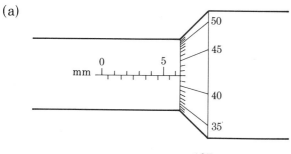

137

(b)

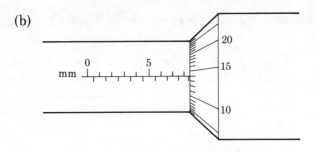

(c)

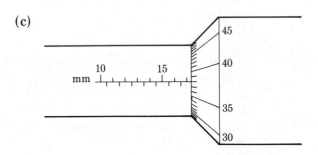

⑩ Georgina paid a bill for £460 using only £10 and £20 notes. There were 26 notes altogether. How many of each were there?

Exercise 51

① Complete each diagram so that the number in any square is the sum of the numbers in the two circles on opposite sides of that square.

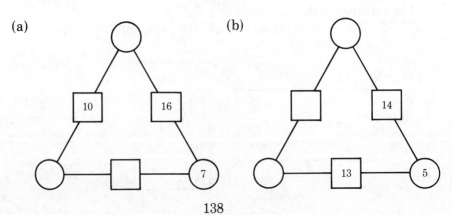

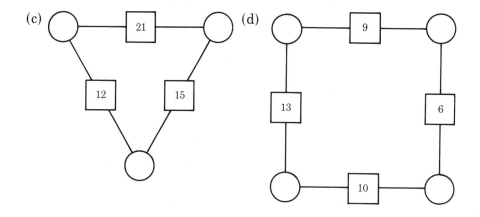

(c) (d)

(2) Yvette writes down three numbers. When she adds them in pairs the totals are 42, 50 and 54. Which three numbers did Yvette write down?

(3) A company bought two earth moving machines and sold them when they ceased to be of further use. Each machine was sold for £60 000. On the first machine they made a profit of 20% but on the second they suffered a loss of 20%. Find the cost price of each machine. Did they make a profit or a loss on the whole transaction?

(4) Find the smallest positive whole number that, when divided by 5 gives a remainder of 3, and when divided by 8 gives a remainder of 2.

(5)

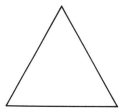

Arrange nine equilateral triangles to give a shape with:

(a) the shortest possible perimeter
(b) the longest possible perimeter.

The triangles must be placed with a complete edge in contact with a complete edge,

i.e. 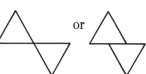 is acceptable but   or   is not.

(6)

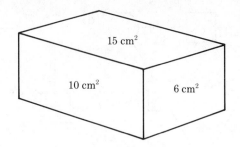

Jenny has a small rectangular cardboard box. The areas of three adjacent faces of this box are shown in the sketch. Find:

(a) the dimensions of the faces
(b) the capacity of the box.

(7)

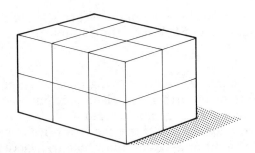

The sketch shows a stack of cubes.

(a) How many cubes are there?
(b) How many exposed faces are there in the stack?
(c) How many unexposed faces are there?
(d) Can you restack the cubes so that twice as many faces are exposed as in the sketch?
(e) What is the maximum number of faces that can be exposed completely if the cubes are stacked in a single pile?

(In all parts of this question, each face is exposed completely or not at all.)

(8) (a) A coin can be placed on a table in one of two ways, i.e. showing either the head (H) or the tail (T). Two coins can be arranged in a row in four different ways. Two of them are HH and HT. What are the other two?

(b) How many different ways are there for arranging:
(i) 3 (ii) 4 (iii) 5,
coins in a row?

(c)

Number of coins in row	1	2	3	4	5
Number of arrangements	2	4			

Copy and complete this table.

140

Use the pattern from the table to write down the number of different arrangements if there are:
(i) 6 coins (ii) 10 coins.
(d) How many coins are there if the total number of arrangements is:
(i) 256 (ii) 1024?

⑨

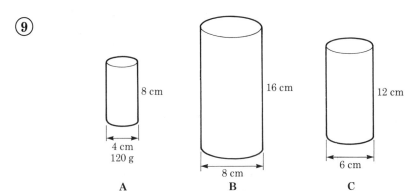

A   B   C

A supermarket stocks tins of dried milk powder in three sizes. The tins are similar in shape and their dimensions are shown in the sketches. The smallest tin (**A**) holds 120 g.

(a) What weight will tin **B** hold?
(b) What weight will tin **C** hold?

⑩ At the inaugural meeting of a committee, sixty-six handshakes were exchanged. Each person shook hands exactly once with each of the others. How large was the committee? Could there be a problem in electing a chairperson?

Exercise 52

① A particular type of paper is 0.25 mm thick. What is the height, in metres, of a stack of 10 000 sheets of this paper?

② The postage on a rather large first class letter is 90 p. Can Vera pay the correct postage using only 5 p and 7 p stamps? Is there more than one way of doing this?

③ A factory owner died and left the sum of £510 000 to be divided among his widow, three daughters and four sons. Each son was to receive twice as much as a daughter and the widow was to receive three times as much as a son. How much did the widow receive?

④

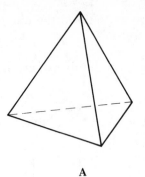 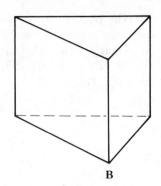

A   B

The diagrams show a pyramid (A) and a triangular prism (B).

(a) For each solid write down:
    (i) the number of edges   (ii) the number of faces.

(b) The pyramid is now placed on top of the prism and fits exactly to form a third solid C. For the solid C:
    (i) how many edges does it have?
    (ii) how many faces does it have?

(c) Explain why your answers to part (b) cannot be found by adding together your answers to part (a).

⑤ (a) Copy and complete the first ten rows of the pattern:

$$1 \qquad\qquad\qquad = \frac{1 \times 2}{2} = 1$$

$$1 + 2 \qquad\qquad = \frac{2 \times 3}{2} = 3$$

$$1 + 2 + 3 \qquad\quad = \frac{3 \times 4}{2} = 6$$

$$1 + 2 + 3 + 4 \qquad = \frac{4 \times 5}{2} = 10$$

$$1 + 2 + 3 + 4 + 5 = \frac{5 \times 6}{2} = 15$$

(b) Use the pattern to find the sum of all the whole numbers from 1 up to:
    (i) 15   (ii) 20   (iii) 40   (iv) 100.

(c) Starting with 1, how many consecutive whole numbers have been added together if the total is:

    (i) $\dfrac{12 \times 13}{2}$ (ii) $\dfrac{45 \times 46}{2}$ (iii) 33×17 (iv) 63×32

    (v) 190   (vi) 378   (vii) 946   (viii) 4371?

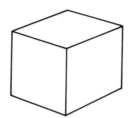

(a) How many vertices does a cube have?
(b) Two vertices of a cube are joined by a straight line. How many different lengths of line are possible?

(7)

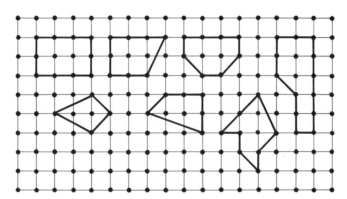

(a) Each polygon in the diagram above surrounds exactly two dots. Draw some more polygons that surround exactly two dots.
(b) Find a rule connecting the area of each shape (i.e. the number of small squares within its boundaries) and the number of dots on its boundary.
(c) A polygon has two dots inside it and 12 on its boundary. What is its area?
(d) A polygon has two dots inside it and has an area of 12 small squares. How many dots are there on its boundary?

(8)

Sim stands in front of a cubical box which has an edge of length 1 metre. He pivots the box about the bottom edge nearest him. Sketch the path traced out by the point A as the box is rotated four times about the bottom edge nearest Sim, by which time the point A has returned to the position shown in the sketch.

143

⑨ The table gives the times taken to complete different numbers of laps of a motor racing circuit for average speeds of 120 m.p.h., 122 m.p.h. and 124 m.p.h.

Average speed in miles per hour (m.p.h.)	Time taken for:				
	1 lap	2 laps	3 laps	4 laps	5 laps
120	1 min 15s	2 min 30s	3 min 45s		6 min 15s
122	1 min 14s	2 min 28s	3 min 42s		6 min 10s
124	1 min 13s	2 min 36s	3 min 39s		6 min 5s

(a) Use the table to find the time taken to do:
   (i) 3 laps at 122 m.p.h.
   (ii) 2 laps at 124 m.p.h.
   (iii) 5 laps at 120 m.p.h.
(b) Copy the table and complete the missing entries.
(c) How long would it take to cover:
   (i) 10 laps at 120 m.p.h.
   (ii) 12 laps at 122 m.p.h.
   (iii) 20 laps at 124 m.p.h.?
(d)   (i) Express 15 seconds as a decimal fraction of one minute.
   (ii) Express 1 min 15 s as a decimal fraction of one hour.
   (iii) Find, correct to one decimal place, the distance in miles around the track.
(e)   (i) How long does it take to cover 60 laps at an average speed of 120 m.p.h.
   (ii) If a 60-lap race starts at 2 p.m., at what time does a driver who averages 120 m.p.h. finish the race?

⑩

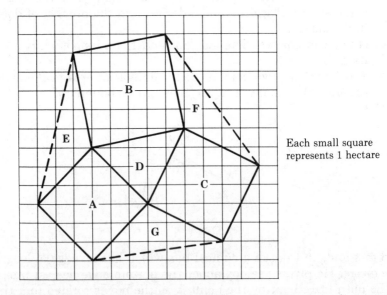

Each small square represents 1 hectare

Major Lord draws a plan of his estate on squared paper. A copy of this plan is shown above. It consists of seven fields: three square ones

144

marked A, B and C, and four triangular ones marked D, E, F and G.

(a) Find   (i) the area of each square field
            (ii) the area of each triangular field.
(b) What is the total area of the estate?

Exercise 53

①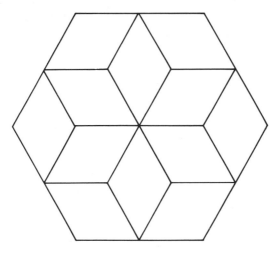

Study this geometrical pattern.

(a) How many quadrilaterals can you see?
(b) How many hexagons (six-sided polygons) can you see?

② A multistorey car park takes $1\frac{1}{4}$ hours to fill at a rate of eight cars per minute.

(a) How many cars does it hold?
(b) How long would it take to fill at a rate of:
    (i) ten cars a minute
    (ii) four cars a minute?

At noon the car park is full. From noon until 3 p.m. cars arrive at the rate of eight cars a minute and leave at the rate of ten cars a minute.

(c) How many cars are there in the car park at:
    (i) 1 p.m.
    (ii) 3 p.m.?

③ Which is the better paid job and by how much:

(a) £165 per week
(b) £9300 per annum
(c) £720 per calendar month?
(Assume that there are 52 weeks in a year.)

④ After all taxes and debts had been paid the value of Mr Snatcher's estate was £170 000. He directed that this should be divided among his widow, four sons and three daughters. Each son was to receive twice as much as each daughter. Each daughter to receive three times as much as the widow.
How much did each daughter receive?

⑤ Monsieur Claude placed one small wine glass and one large wine glass in front of him on the table. The capacity of the large glass was exactly twice that of the small glass. He poured wine into each glass until the small glass was half full and the large glass was one-third full. Next he topped up both glasses with water. Finally he tipped the contents of both glasses into a tumbler. What fraction of the liquid in the tumbler was wine?

⑥

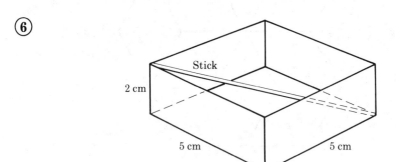

Kathryn has a rectangular box measuring 5 cm by 5 cm by 2 cm into which she can just fit a straight stick, as shown in the diagram. How long is the stick? Brian has a stick that is exactly the same length and he says that his stick will just fit into the rectangular box he has, but that the dimensions of his box (although also whole numbers of centimetres) are different from those of Kathryn's box. What are the dimensions of Brian's box?

⑦ The vet put Sandy, my old golden retriever, on eye drops. The dosage was 1.25 ml each day. He gave me a bottle containing 100 ml. About how many weeks should this bottle have lasted?

⑧ You've probably noticed that at 3 o'clock and 9 o'clock the hands of a clock are at right angles to each other. How many times from 12 noon to 12 midnight are the hands of a clock at right angles to each other?

⑨ The diagram shows part of the road plan of a Canadian city. The residential quarter is in the West and the business quarter is in the East.

146

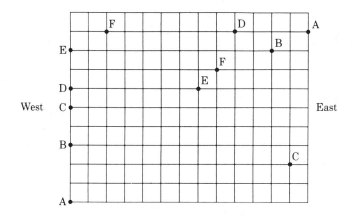

Points A to E, on the left-hand side of the diagram, show where five people live. The letters on the right-hand side show where each person works, e.g. A lives at the bottom left-hand corner of the grid and works near the top right-hand corner. Show how it is possible for each person to travel from home to work along the grid lines without crossing any other person's path.

⑩

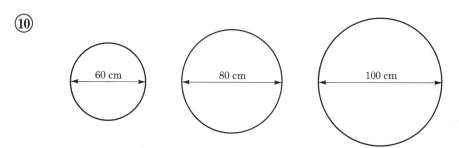

Mrs Price bought three circular table cloths in a sale. Their diameters were 60 cm, 80 cm and 100 cm. She wanted to divide the three cloths into four pieces with equal areas. Eventually she succeeded in doing this by making just two cuts. Can you show how she did it?

⑪

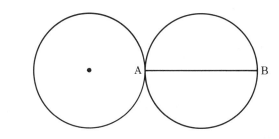

A 10 p coin is rolled without slipping all the way round the edge of another 10 p coin, which is fixed. The coins are originally in contact at A where AB is a diameter. Through what angle does AB turn?

147

Exercise 54

① When Natasha is working she always goes to bed at the same time and sleeps for the same number of hours. She goes to bed at 11.30 p.m. and her watch then needs five turns to become fully wound. When she awakes the following morning the watch needs a further three turns to become fully wound again. What time does she get up in the morning?

② When we write 5 200 000 as 5.2×10^6 or 0.00052 as 5.2×10^{-4} we say that we have written each number in standard form.

(a) The mean distance of the planet Pluto from the Sun is 5907 million kilometres. Express this number in standard form.

(b) The diameter of a particle is 0.000007 cm. Express the diameter in standard form.

③ Using the signs $+ - \times$ and $\div$, arrange four 3s to give each of the whole numbers from 1 to 10.

For example, $\dfrac{3 + 3}{3 + 3} = 1$ and $\dfrac{3}{3} + \dfrac{3}{3} = 2$.

④ The sums of three numbers taken in pairs are 52, 60 and 66. What is the smallest number?

⑤ The distance between London and Birmingham is 111 miles. A slow train leaves London at 1012 and arrives in Birmingham at 1212. On the same day an InterCity 125 leaves Birmingham at 1012 and arrives in London at 1112. Where and when do they pass?

⑥ Nick wishes to choose weights that will enable him to use his old-fashioned scales to weigh goods for all the whole number weights from 1 kg to 40 kg. He is offered a set with the following weights:

1 kg   2 kg   4 kg   8 kg   16 kg   32 kg.

Charlotte tells him that there is no need to buy a set with so many different weights. She says that she has seen a set with just four weights, but that this set means that sometimes it is necessary to put weights on both scale pans. What are the four weights?

148

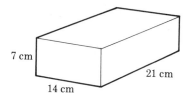

Danny has a supply of building blocks, each measuring 21 cm by
14 cm by 7 cm. Some of these blocks are placed together in a stack to
form a solid cube. What is the least number of blocks required?
Assume that there are no spaces between the blocks.

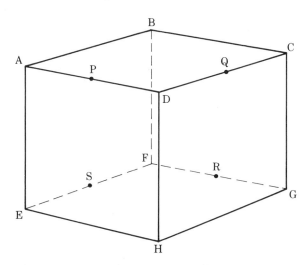

The diagram shows a cube ABCDEFGH. P, Q, R and S are the mid-
points of the edges AD, DC, FG and EF, respectively.
Draw the shape of the section made by cutting the cube along each of
the following planes:

(a) a plane through Q parallel to the face ADHE
(b) ACGE
(c) PQH
(d) EPQG
(e) PQRS.

(When convenient, you can check any of these by making a cube from
 a potato and cutting it along the appropriate plane.)

(9) An international oil company has offices in Paris, Tokyo and New
York. The Paris office is open from 8.00 a.m to 4.30 p.m. The New
York office is open from 8.30 a.m. to 4 p.m. and the Tokyo office is
open from 8.30 a.m. to 5.30 p.m. (All times are local times.) The time
in Tokyo is 8 hours ahead of Paris and the time in New York is 6
hours behind Paris.

(a) What is the earliest time that the Paris office can ring the New
York office?

(b) For how many hours in the day are both the Paris and New York offices open together?

(c) How many hours are there in the day when all three offices are closed?

⑩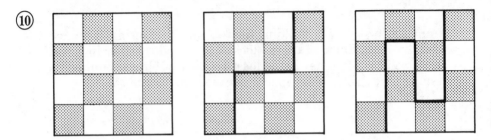

In how many different ways can a square chequered board with 16 squares be divided into two parts of the same size and shape by cuts along the lines dividing the squares? Two possible ways are shown. If you would like a tougher problem try a similar one for a board with 36 squares.

Exercise 55

① Lesley thinks of a number. When she divides that number by 8 the answer is 7, with a remainder of 5. What number did Lesley think of?

② When Trudy Burke retires she can expect to receive a tax-free lump sum of $3 \times N$ eightieths of her final year's salary, together with an annual pension of one third of her lump sum. N stands for the number of years she works for the firm.

(a) If she retired after 20 years and was then earning £16 000 p.a., what pension and lump sum could she expect?

(b) Suppose she stayed for 40 years and earned £30 000 during her final year. What would her annual pension be then?

③ If eight is three less than two too many, how many is enough?

④ A small group of school friends go to a department store to buy some tapes to give as Christmas presents. Each friend buys the same number of £5 tapes and each friend buys the same number of £7 tapes. Between them they spend £138. How many friends are there and how many of each price of tape do they buy?

⑤ Santo is given a set of six coloured plastic cubes for his birthday. The smallest cube has an edge of 1 cm, the next in size has a 2 cm edge, and so on, until the largest cube has an edge of 6 cm. He builds them into two towers.

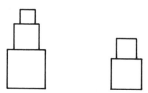

(a) Can he build two towers of equal height? Give a reason for your answer.
(b) Would an additional cube with an edge of 8 cm help?
(c) What can you say about the length of the edge of an additional seventh cube that Santo could be given so that he can make two towers with equal heights?

⑥

Sixteen different quadrilaterals can be made by joining the dots on this grid. Sketch each one. Indicate which one has:
(a) the smallest area   (b) the largest area.

⑦ (a) Using British coins in circulation, show how you could make up each of the following amounts exactly:
      (i) 13 p   (ii) 55 p   (iii) 37 p.
(b) Show how you can make up   (i) 82 p   (ii) 58 p, without using more than one coin of each value.
(c) How can you make up   (i) 75 p   (ii) 44 p using the least number of coins?

⑧ Four numbers are written on two discs, one on each side of each disc. By spinning the two discs and adding together the numbers that fall uppermost the possible totals are 8, 9, 10 or 11. Find the numbers on each disc.

(9) The table shows the travel and accommodation costs for a holiday in a country cottage in northern France in the summer.

YOUR HOLIDAY PRICES INCLUDE: RETURN CHANNEL FERRY CROSSING WITH CAR AND 7 OR 14 NIGHTS ACCOMMODATION. **CHILDREN UNDER 4 FREE**

LENGTH OF STAY	ONE WEEK				TWO WEEKS				FRI. OR SAT. U.K. DEPART. SUPPLEMENT PER CAR
£'s PER PERSON IN PARTY OF: (min 2 adults)	ADULTS			CHILD 4–13	ADULTS			CHILD 4–13	
	4	3	2		4	3	2		
20 MAY – 9 JUNE	85	104	144	13	152	187	262	21	13
10 JUNE – 23 JUNE	89	108	149	14	162	198	278	24	15
24 JUNE – 7 JULY	96	116	159	17	174	212	293	28	18
8 JULY – 21 JULY	128	158	221	18	237	294	414	30	19
22 JULY – 18 AUG	137	167	233	20	251	309	433	34	22
19 AUG – 1 SEPT	131	161	225	19	242	299	420	31	20
2 SEPT – 15 SEPT	96	116	159	17	174	212	293	28	15
16 SEPT – 29 SEPT	83	101	140	12	152	187	262	21	—

(DEPARTURE ON OR BETWEEN)

Note that the last column indictes that it costs extra to travel at the weekend.

(a) How much will a two-week holiday cost two adults if they leave on Friday 10 June?

(b) How much will a one-week holiday cost four adults if they leave on Wednesday 12 August?

(c) Mr and Mrs Arnott, and their three children aged 7, 10 and 12, book a two-week holiday leaving on the first Sunday in August. How much will it cost them?

(d) The Thompson family, consisting of father, mother, Anne (aged 5) and Hetty (aged 2), leave for a two-week holiday on Friday 11 June. Find the total cost.

(e) Mr and Mrs Sweet and their son Thomas (aged 16) plan a two-week holiday leaving on Monday 7 September. How much will this cost them?

(10) The total of the scores on the opposite faces of a fair dice is always 7. A net to make such a dice is shown below.

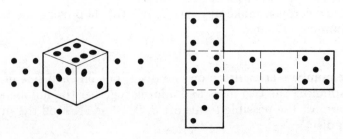

(a) Two such dice are placed one above the other as shown. What is the total score on the faces that are:
(i) exposed   (ii) concealed?

(b) Repeat part (a) for the arrangement shown below.

(c) Three such dice are placed in a row as shown. What is the total score on the faces that are:
(i) exposed   (ii) concealed?

(d) Is it possible to place four dice in a row so that the total of the scores on the exposed faces is equal to the total of the scores on the hidden faces?

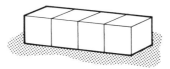

Part B TOPIC-BASED EXERCISES

Exercise 56 Angles and Parallel Lines

Find the size of each marked angle.

1
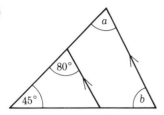

5
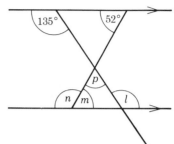

2
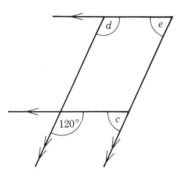

6
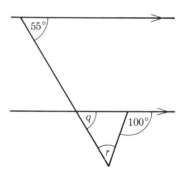

3
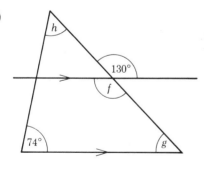

7
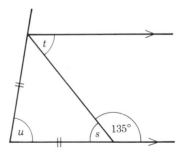

4
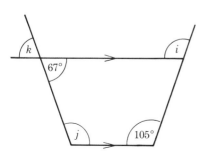

8
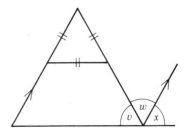

157

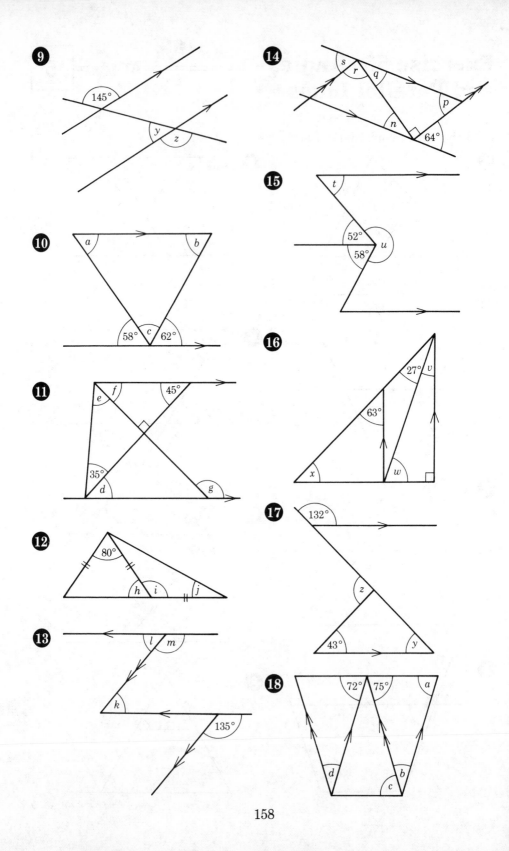

9

145°

y z

10

a b

58° c 62°

11

e f 45°

35°
d g

12

80°

h i j

13

l m

k

135°

14

s r q

n

64°

p

15

t

52°
u
58°

16

27° v

63°

x w

17

132°

z

43° y

18

72° 75° a

d b

c

158

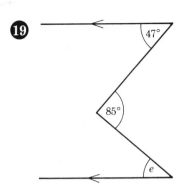

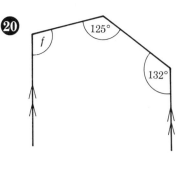

Exercise 57 Decimals ═══════AT $\mathbf{2}$═4–6

1 What is the value of the figure 5 in each of the following numbers:
   (a) 33.5   (b) 15.2   (c) 53.7   (d) 46.25?

2 Write each set of numbers in order of size with the smallest number first.
   (a) 3.7, 3.07, 3.77   (c) 51.72, 57.21, 52.17, 51.27
   (b) 12.06, 21.6, 16.2   (d) 9.42, 9.04, 9.24, 9.22

3 For each set of numbers given below write down:
   (i) the largest   (ii) the smallest.
   (a) 9.71, 2.79, 7.92, 27.9   (c) 46.2, 4.620, 6.24, 24.6, 46.06
   (b) 2.4, 2.04, 4.20, 2.41   (d) 1.55, 0.55, 5.01, 10.5, 0.51

4 Write as fractions in their lowest terms:
   (a) 0.5   (d) 0.3   (g) 0.066
   (b) 0.25   (e) 0.4   (h) 0.72
   (c) 0.75   (f) 0.55   (i) 0.375

5 Find:
   (a) 4.72 + 1.26   (d) 4.7 + 0.09   (g) 8.21 + 1.054 + 2.7
   (b) 0.15 + 0.015   (e) 8.2 + 0.004   (h) 0.64 + 0.064 + 0.006
   (c) 7.24 + 4.1   (f) 3.45 + 0.742   (i) 1.25 + 0.125 + 0.0125

6 Find:
   (a) 10 − 7.2   (d) 4 − 3.79   (g) 0.464 − 0.089
   (b) 8.6 − 5.4   (e) 7.5 − 2.92   (h) 105.7 − 58.6
   (i) 16.3 − 5.14   (f) 6.92 − 1.09   (i) 37.2 − 14.08

7 Find the value of::

(a) 56 × 100
(b) 3.47 × 10
(c) 0.29 × 100

(d) 0.048 × 10
(e) 1.07 × 100
(f) 0.08 × 1000

(g) 29.3 × 1000
(h) 0.0064 × 100
(i) 0.0816 × 10 000

8 Find the value of:

(a) 93 ÷ 10
(b) 54 ÷ 100
(c) 7.2 ÷ 100

(d) 0.4 ÷ 10
(e) 0.272 ÷ 100
(f) 4.08 ÷ 1000

(g) 16.09 ÷ 100
(h) 6.39 ÷ 10
(i) 0.36 ÷ 1000

9 Find the value of:

(a) 2.58 ÷ 2
(b) 1.8 ÷ 6
(c) 27.5 ÷ 5

(d) 4.9 ÷ 7
(e) 0.0618 ÷ 6
(f) 0.0028 ÷ 4

(g) 5.44 ÷ 8
(h) 0.00065 ÷ 5
(i) 292 ÷ 8

10 Find the value of:

(a) 15.6 ÷ 12
(b) 40.5 ÷ 15
(c) 121.8 ÷ 21

(d) 15.4 ÷ 35
(e) 77.4 ÷ 43
(f) 7.28 ÷ 14

(g) 81.6 ÷ 17
(h) 15.4 ÷ 28
(i) 21.85 ÷ 23

11 Calculate the following products:

(a) 0.3 × 0.7
(b) 0.4 × 0.5
(c) 0.1 × 0.1

(d) 0.07 × 5
(e) 4 × 0.08
(f) 0.8 × 0.04

(g) 0.04 × 0.08
(h) 0.5 × 0.03
(i) 0.006 × 3

12 Calculate the following products:

(a) 42 × 0.34
(b) 34.6 × 24
(c) 13.7 × 5.6

(d) 0.046 × 0.79
(e) 0.28 × 0.28
(f) 7.2 × 2.7

(g) 5.7 × 0.75
(h) 0.38 × 0.045
(i) 212 × 3.06

13 Give the following numbers correct to two decimal places:

(a) 1.278
(b) 0.092
(c) 7.955

(d) 0.421
(e) 0.008
(f) 10.094

(g) 5.999
(h) 20.737
(i) 18.004

14 Give the following numbers correct to the nearest whole number:

(a) 6.84
(b) 13.7
(c) 34.5

(d) 3.09
(e) 107.48
(f) 8.625

(g) 3.099
(h) 3.999
(i) 81.55

15 Give the following fractions either as exact decimals or correct to three decimal places:

(a) $\frac{3}{8}$
(b) $\frac{11}{25}$
(c) $\frac{4}{5}$

(d) $\frac{5}{7}$
(c) $\frac{3}{17}$
(f) $\frac{1}{9}$

(g) $\frac{15}{22}$
(l) $\frac{6}{13}$
(i) $\frac{7}{11}$

Exercise 58 Percentages ===AT 2=4,6

1 Write the first number as a percentage of the second number:
  (a) 50 out of 100   (d) 25 out of 100   (g) 40 out of 80
  (b) 75 out of 100   (e) 25 out of 50   (h) 40 out of 40
  (c) 40 out of 100   (f) 15 out of 20   (i) 100 out of 100.

2 In this question copy each diagram and then carry out the instruction.

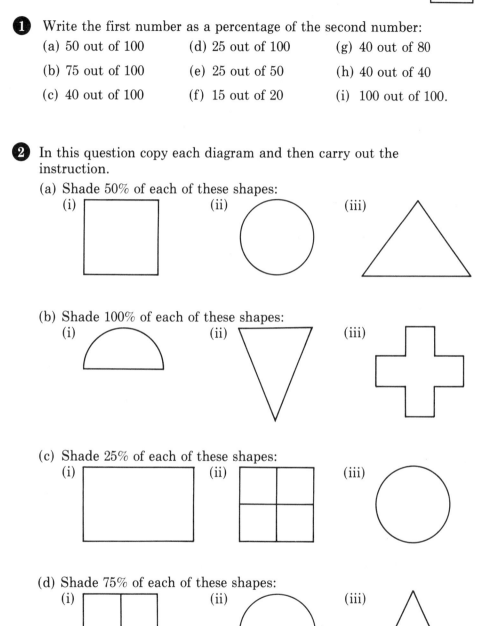

  (a) Shade 50% of each of these shapes:
      (i)   (ii)   (iii)

  (b) Shade 100% of each of these shapes:
      (i)   (ii)   (iii)

  (c) Shade 25% of each of these shapes:
      (i)   (ii)   (iii)

  (d) Shade 75% of each of these shapes:
      (i)   (ii)   (iii)

3 Copy and complete each statement:

(a) 10 people out of 20 people is ____ %

(b) £5 out of £20 is ____ %

(c) 7 marks out of 10 is ____ %

(d) 9 cars out of 12 cars is ____ %.

4 Copy and complete each sentence:

(a) 50% of 24 sweets is ____ sweets

(b) 25% of 16 bicycles is ____ bicycles

(c) 50% of 180 spectators is ____ spectators

(d) 25% of 40 minutes is ____ minutes

(e) 75% of 12 months is ____ months.

5 (a) What percentage is 44 out of 100?

(b) Write $\frac{53}{100}$ as a percentage.

(c) What is 40 p as a percentage of 50 p?

(d) What is 25% of 12 hours?

(e) Write $\frac{10}{100}$ as a percentage.

6 Two oranges in a bag of eight oranges are bad. What percentage is this?

7 There are eight slices in a packet of garlic bread. When six slices have been eaten:

(a) what percentage of the garlic bread has been eaten?

(b) what percentage of it remains?

8 Sandra received 24 birthday cards, 25% of which had been sent by first class post.

(a) How many of Sandra's cards had been sent by first class post?

(b) How many of Sandra's cards had not been sent by first class post?

9 Bill's newspaper has 32 pages. He has looked at 24 of them.

(a) What percentage of the newspaper has he looked at?

(b) What percentage has he not looked at?

10 David and Sue bought a pack of 48 old postcards. David wanted 24 of them, Sue wanted 12 of them and the remainder were thrown away.

(a) What percentage of the postcards did David want?

(b) What percentage of the postcards did Sue want?

(c) What percentage were thrown away?

Exercise 59 Coordinates

1 Write down the coordinates of the points A, B, C, D, E, F, G and H on the diagram below.

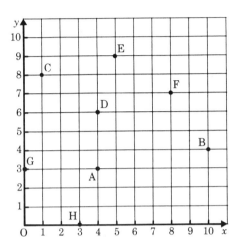

2 Draw a set of axes and scale each one from 0 to 10. Mark the following points: A(3, 7), B(4, 10), C(5, 7), D(8, 6), E(5, 5), F(4, 2), G(3, 5) and H(0, 6).
Now join the points in alphabetical order and join H to A. Describe the figure you get. Write down the coordinates of the centre of this shape.

3 Draw a set of axes and scale each one from 0 to 10.
(a) Mark the points A(1, 4), B(5, 8) and C(7, 2). Join the points to make a triangle.
(b) Find the mid-point of AB and mark it D. Write down the coordinates of D.
(c) Find the mid-point of AC and mark it E. Write down the coordinates of E.
(d) Measure the lengths of BC and DE. How do their lengths compare?

4 On a set of axes marked from 0 to 10, plot the points A(2, 7), B(7, 6), C(6, 1) and D(1, 2). Join the points to make a quadrilateral ABCD. What is the name of ABCD?
Write down the coordinates of the centre of this quadrilateral.

163

5 Three corners of a rectangle ABCD are the points A(3, 0), B(1, 4) and C(7, 7).

(a) By plotting these points on axes marked from 0 to 10, find the coordinates of the fourth corner D.

(b) On the line BC, mark a point E that is twice as far from C as it is from B.

(c) Mark F, the mid-point of CD.

(d) Join EF. How is EF related to the x-axis?

6 Write down the coordinates of the points A, B, C, D, E, F, G and H on the diagram below.

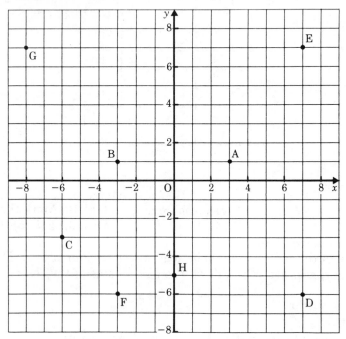

In questions 7 to 10 draw your own sets of axes and scale each one from −7 to 8.

7 Mark the points A(−3, 1), B(4, 3), C(2, −4) and D(−5, −6). Join the points to give a quadrilateral ABCD. What is the special name of this quadrilateral?

8 Mark the points A(−4, 7), B(−7, −2) and C(5, −6). Join the points to give the figure ABC. Describe ABC. Find the coordinates of D if ABCD is a rectangle.

9 ABCD is a square labelled in a clockwise direction. A is the point (−5, 1) and C is the point (7, 1). Use a suitable diagram to find:

(a) the coordinates of M, the mid-point of AC

(b) the coordinates of B and D.

164

10 Plot the points A(−3, 5), B(3, 3), C(7, −5) and D(−5, −1). Join the points to give a quadrilateral. What name do we give to this type of quadrilateral? Join AC and BD. If M is the mid-point of BD and N is the mid-point of AC, write down the coordinates of M and N. Join MN. How is this line related to AB and CD?

Exercise 60 Symmetry ═══════AT ▲ = 3-5

1 Copy the following drawings on to squared paper and complete them so that each dashed line is an axis of symmetry.

(a)

(d)
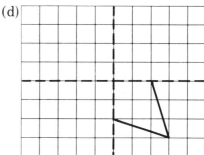

(b)
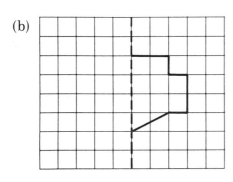

(e)
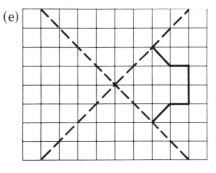

(c)
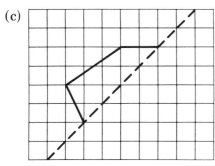

(f)
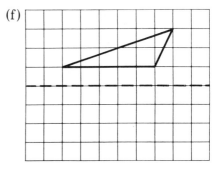

(g)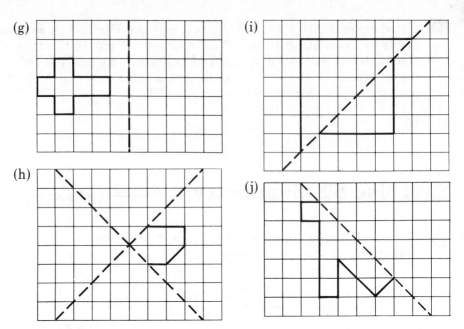

(i)

(h)

(j)

2 Copy the diagrams and draw the mirror lines, i.e. the lines of symmetry, such that the dashed mirror image is a reflection of the solid figure.

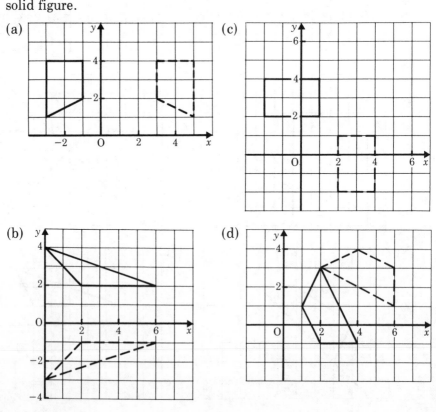

(a)

(c)

(b)

(d)

166

3 Which of the following shapes have rotational symmetry? For any shape that does, give the order of its rotational symmetry. (You may find it useful to trace the shape and then turn it about the centre of rotation.)

(a)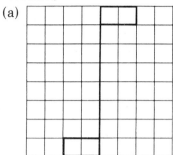

(d)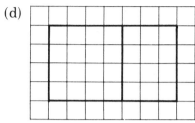

(b)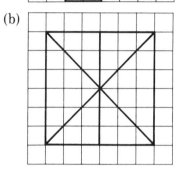

(e)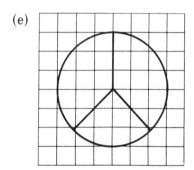

(c)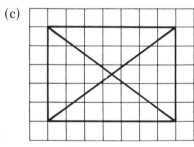

(f)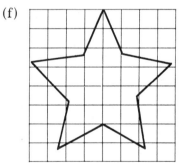

4 Each of the diagrams given below, when completed has rotational symmetry of the order given. The X marks the centre of rotation. Copy and complete each diagram allowing sufficient space on your squared paper.

(a)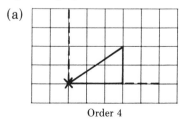

Order 4

(b)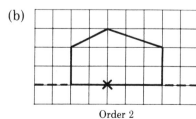

Order 2

167

(c)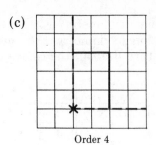

Order 4

(d)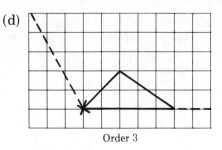

Order 3

(e)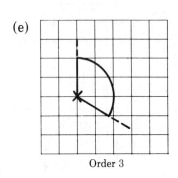

Order 3

(f)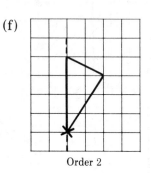

Order 2

5 Which of the following shapes have:
   (i) line symmetry only
   (ii) rotational symmetry only
   (iii) both?

(a)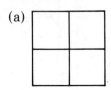

(c)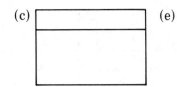

(e)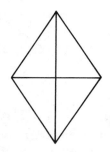

(b)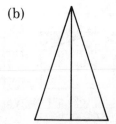

(d)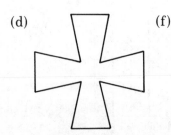

(f)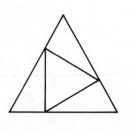

6 On squared paper copy and complete the shape drawn below so that the resulting shape has rotational symmetry of order 4. A is the centre of rotation.

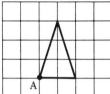

Does the resulting shape have line symmetry?

7 For each diagram give the coordinates of the centre of rotation and the angle of rotation if the solid triangle is mapped to the dashed triangle.

(a)
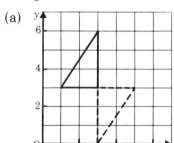

(d)
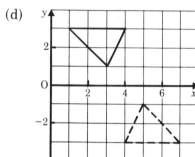

(b)
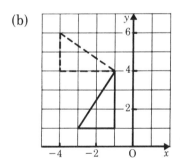

(e)
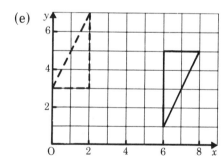

(c)
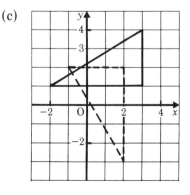

(f)
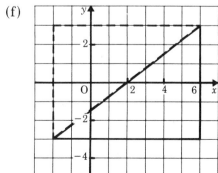

8 Copy the diagram given below on to squared paper and use it to find the images of the given object under the rotations described.

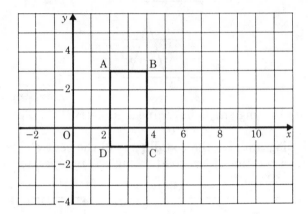

(a) Centre of rotation A, angle of rotation 90° clockwise.
(b) Centre of rotation C, angle of rotation 90° anticlockwise.
(c) Centre of rotation the mid-point of BC, angle of rotation 180°.
(d) Centre of rotation (6, 4), angle of rotation 90° anticlockwise.

9

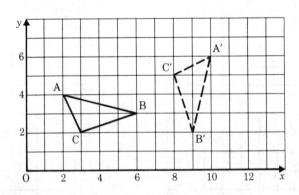

Copy the diagram on to squared paper using a scale of 1 cm to 1 unit. △A′B′C′ is the image of △ABC under a rotation.

(a) Draw the perpendicular bisectors of AA′ and BB′, and hence find the centre of rotation. Mark it X.
(b) Join BX and B′X. What is the angle of rotation?

170

Exercise 61 Statistics 1 ═══ AT 5 = 3-5

1 This frequency table shows the results of asking a group of pupils their favourite subject on the school timetable.

Subject	Geography	French	English	Maths	CDT	Games
Frequency	6	5	9	8	7	8

(a) How many pupils were there in the group?
(b) What was the most popular subject?
(c) Draw a bar chart to show this information.

2 For a Maths project, Jean was asked to investigate the number of letters per word on a page of a book. Her results are given below.

5	4	7	4	5	8	10	5	1	4
3	4	5	2	4	9	4	5	3	4
5	3	3	8	6	9	6	11	5	5
9	1	7	4	2	1	4	6	7	6
5	6	2	4	5	6	4	3	5	2
4	4	8	6	4	5	2	13	4	4
3	1	6	5	4					

(a) How many words were there on the page?
(b) Copy and complete this frequency table.

Number of letters	Tally	Frequency
1–3		
4–6		
7–9		
10–12		
13–15		

3 A tomato grower counted the number of ripe tomatoes on each of his plants at noon on a particular day. The results are listed below.

8	3	8	7	4	2	5	8	4	7
4	5	10	3	5	7	6	9	4	5
4	6	4	8						

(a) Make a frequency table using this information.
(b) Draw a bar chart to illustrate this information.
(c) How many plants had more than four tomatoes?
(d) How many plants had fewer than four tomatoes?
(e) How many plants were there altogether?

4 This pie chart shows the age distribution of the population of a developing country in 1992.

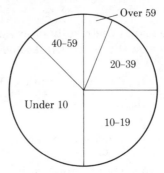

(a) Estimate the fraction of the population in the age group:
    (i) 10–19   (ii) 40–59   (iii) under 10.
(b) If the population of the country is 8 million, estimate the number that are younger than 20.

5 The weights of eight girls are 52 kg, 49 kg, 53 kg, 61 kg, 54 kg, 56 kg, 48 kg and 51 kg. Find:

(a) the range of these weights
(b) the mean weight.

6 A group of third-year pupils sat a science assessment test. Their marks are listed below.

$$15 \quad 13 \quad 4 \quad 15 \quad 15 \quad 19 \quad 14 \quad 16$$
$$17 \quad 9 \quad 7 \quad 14 \quad 18 \quad 12 \quad 12 \quad 8$$

Find: (a) the range of these marks
        (b) the mean mark.

7 The distance, in miles, travelled by twelve different cars of a particular model on one gallon of petrol under test conditions, are given below.

$$33 \quad 38 \quad 36 \quad 42 \quad 38 \quad 34.5$$
$$34 \quad 37.5 \quad 37 \quad 36 \quad 35 \quad 37$$

Find: (a) the range of these distances
        (b) the mean distance travelled.

8 The mean height of a group of twelve 14-year-old boys is 151 cm. The heights of eleven of these boys are given below.

157 cm   135 cm   147 cm   178 cm   138 cm   155 cm
155 cm   169 cm   164 cm   148 cm   135 cm

(a) What is the total of the heights of the twelve boys?
(b) What is the height of the twelfth boy?
(c) Find the range of these heights.

Exercise 62 Directed Numbers AT = 5

1 Which temperature is higher:
(a) 1° or −4°   (c) −3° or 4°   (e) −7° or −3°
(b) −5° or −2°   (d) −1° or 1°   (f) 5° or −1°?

2 Write either > or < between each pair of numbers:
(a) 3   1   (c) 6   −9   (e) −3   0
(b) 4   −1   (d) −5   −8   (f) −7   2

3 Using a number line if it helps, find:
(a) 5 − 7   (d) −(+2) − (+4)   (g) (+4) − (+7) + (+2)
(b) −4 + 2   (e) 2 + 9 − 10   (h) (+3) − (+5) − (+7)
(c) (+3) − (+4)   (f) 3 − 5 − 8   (i) −(+5) + (+3) − (+9)

4 Find:
(a) 4 + (−2)   (e) (−1) + (−2) + (−3)   (i) 9 + (−3) − (+2)
(b) 7 − (−3)   (f) 5 − (−3) + (−2)   (j) 4 − (+3) + (−5)
(c) −5 + (−5)   (g) 8 − (−5) − (−3)   (k) −2 + (+4) + (−7)
(d) −2 − (−6)   (h) −6 + (−4) − (−3)   (l) −6 − (+5) − (−9)

5 Find the following products:
(a) 5 × (−3)   (d) (−8) × 2   (g) (−5) × 1
(b) 4 × (−7)   (e) (+2) × (−5)   (h) (−4) × 1.5
(c) (−6) × 3   (f) (−1) × (+6)   (i) 3 × (−2.5)

6 Find:
(a) (−8) ÷ 2   (d) (−4) ÷ 4   (g) $-\frac{36}{12}$
(b) (−12) ÷ 3   (e) (−21) ÷ (+7)   (h) $-\frac{12}{2}$
(c) (−10) ÷ (+2)   (f) (−30) ÷ (+6)   (i) $-\frac{27}{3}$

7 Find the following products:
(a) (−4) × (−3)   (d) (−3) × (−2)   (g) (−4) × (−6)
(b) 7 × (−7)   (e) (−6) × 5   (h) 5 × (−8)
(c) (−5) × (−2)   (f) (−8) × (−9)   (i) (−8) × 7

8 Find:
(a) (−8) ÷ (−4)   (d) 24 ÷ (−8)   (g) 15 ÷ (−3)
(b) (−12) ÷ (−2)   (e) (−16) ÷ 4   (h) 28 ÷ (−7)
(c) 18 ÷ (−3)   (f) (−36) ÷ (−9)   (i) (−48) ÷ (−12)

9 Rearrange the numbers 3, −8, −2, 4, 0 in order of size, with the smallest first.

173

10 Rearrange the numbers −5, 8, −10, 18, −2 in order of size, with the largest first.

11 At 6 p.m. the temperature was 6 °C. By 2 a.m. it had fallen to −4 °C. By how much had the temperature fallen?

12 The reading on my thermometer at midnight was −2 °C. By 6 a.m. the temperature had fallen by 7 °C. What was the new temperature?

Exercise 63 Metric and and Imperial Conversion

AT **2** = **5**

In questions 1 to 5 express the given quantity in terms of the units given in brackets.

1
(a) 3 kg (g)
(b) 5 km (m)
(c) 7.3 m (cm)
(d) 54 cm (mm)
(e) 0.07 km (cm)
(f) 0.24 m (mm)
(g) 0.36km (m)
(h) 1.64 kg (g)
(i) 8.26 m (cm)

2
(a) 2000 g (kg)
(b) 8000 m (km)
(c) 1500 cm (m)
(d) 840 mm (cm)
(e) 7200 mm (m)
(f) 542 g (kg)
(g) 64 m (km)
(h) 1720 cm (km)
(i) 372 mm (cm)

3
(a) 8 ft (in)
(b) 2 miles (yd)
(c) 5 yd 2 ft (ft)
(d) 4 ft 3 in (in)
(e) 2 ft 11 in (in)
(f) 8 yd 1 ft (in)
(g) 1 yd 5 in (in)
(h) 90 yd 2 ft (ft)
(i) 18 ft 6 in (in)

4
(a) 72 in (ft)
(b) 27 ft (yd)
(c) 144 in (yd)
(d) 44 in (ft and in)
(e) 37 ft (yd and ft)
(f) 3000 yd (miles and yd)
(g) 100 ft (yd and ft)
(h) 200 in (ft and in)
(i) 1500 in (yd, ft and in)

5
(a) 3 lb (oz)
(b) 2 lb 5 oz (oz)
(c) 448 lb (cwt)
(d) 18 oz (lb and oz)
(e) 300 lb (cwt and lb)
(f) 100 oz (lb and oz)
(g) 100 cwt (tons)
(h) 8 tons (cwt)
(i) 150 lb (cwt and lb)

6 If 1 kg ≈ 2 lb, 1 m ≈ 1 yd or 3 ft, 5 miles ≈ 8 km and 1 in ≈ 2.5 cm, convert the given quantity into an approximate number of the units in brackets.
(a) 5 kg (lb)
(b) 4 lb (kg)
(c) 1.5 kg (lb)
(d) 8 m (ft)
(e) 80 km (miles)
(f) 100 miles (km)
(g) 20 in (cm)
(h) 200 cm (in)
(i) 500 g (lb)
(j) 60 cm (ft)
(k) 160 lb (kg)
(l) 1000 km (miles)

Use the approximations given in question 6 to answer questions 7 to 12.

7 Which is heavier: a 5 lb bag of potatoes or four 1 kg packets of sugar?

8 A church window is 24 ft high. Roughly, what is its height in metres?

9 A car is 4.5 m long. Roughly, what is the length of the car in
(a) feet (b) inches?

10 Which has the larger area: a sheet of plywood measuring 2 m by 1 m or one measuring 4 ft by 4 ft?

11 The distance between London and Dover is about 70 miles, and the distance between Ostend and Brussels is about 105 km. Which is the shorter distance?

12 Jerry needs some 5 in bolts. The available sizes are 8 cm, 10 cm, 12 cm, 15 cm and 20 cm. Which size should he buy assuming that he must buy oversize rather than undersize?

13 (a) Cameron buys 25 litres of petrol. How many gallons is this?
    (1 litre = 0.220 gallons)
(b) Sandra buys 8 gallons of red wine. How many litres is this?

14 (a) The area of a farm is 365 acres. How many hectares is this?
    (1 hectare = 2.47 acres)
(b) A French smallholding has an area of 34 hectares. How many acres is this?

15 Given that 1 inch = 2.54 cm convert:
(a) 12 inches into centimetres
(b) 100 centimetres into inches
(c) 1 square inch into square centimetres (cm^2)
(d) 1 cm^2 into square inches
(e) 1 cubic inch into cubic centimetres (cm^3)
(f) 1 cm^3 into cubic inches.

16 If 1 m = 1.09 yd, find the price of a carpet measuring 5 yd by 4 yd and costing £35 per square metre.

17 A lawn measures 35 yd by 24 yd. Fertilizer is to be spread on it with a coverage of 10 g per square metre. How many kilograms of fertilizer is required? Give your answer correct to three significant figures.
(1 m = 1.09 yd)

18 Curtain material is sold at £16.80 per metre in one shop and at £18.15 per yard in another. I need 12 metres. At what price should I buy it? (1 m = 1.09 yd)

Exercise 64 Area ========= AT **4** = **4-7**

1 Find the area of a rectangle measuring:
(a) 12 cm by 7 cm   (c) 4.6 m by 3.5 m

(b) 25 mm by 14 mm   (d) $1\frac{1}{2}$ m by $2\frac{1}{4}$ m.

2 Find the area of a rectangle measuring:
(a) 30 cm by $\frac{1}{2}$ m, giving your answer in cm^2

(b) 720 mm by 43 cm, giving your answer in cm^2

(c) 642 cm by 1.73 m, giving your answer in m^2

(d) 8.4 cm by 33 mm, giving your answer in mm^2.

3 Copy and complete the following table.

	Length	Width	Area
(a)	12 cm		$108\ cm^2$
(b)		3.6 m	$30.6\ m^2$
(c)		2.25 mm	$45.9\ mm^2$
(d)	6.4 cm		$22.4\ cm^2$

4 Find the area of each of the following figures in square centimetres. All measurements are given in centimetres.

(a)

(c)

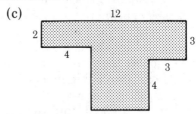

(b)

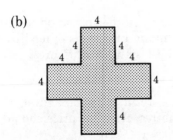

(d)

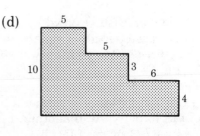

(e)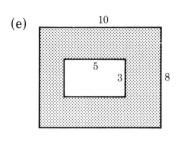

(f)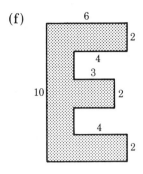

5 Find the area of each of the following triangles.

(a)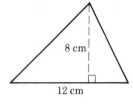

8 cm

12 cm

(c)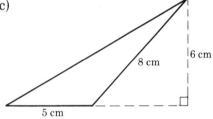

8 cm

6 cm

5 cm

(b)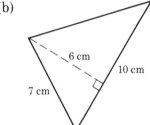

6 cm

10 cm

7 cm

(d)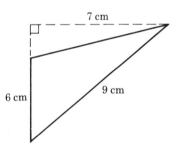

7 cm

6 cm

9 cm

6 The area of a triangle is 36 cm². If it is 8 cm high, find the length of its base.

7 Find the area of each shaded region. All measurements are in centimetres.

(a)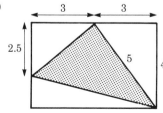

3   3

2.5

5

4

(b)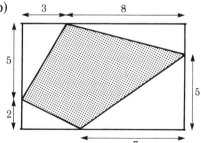

3   8

5

5

2

7

177

8 Find the area of each of the following shapes.

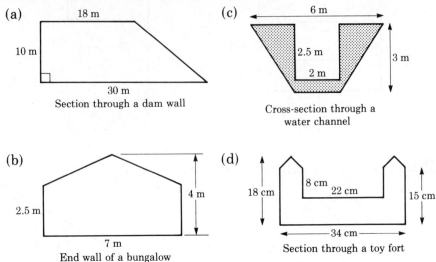

(a)

Section through a dam wall

(b)

End wall of a bungalow

(c)

Cross-section through a
water channel

(d)

Section through a toy fort

In questions 9 to 15 use 3.142 as the approximate value of π or use the π button on your calculator. Give any answers that are not exact to three significant figures.

9 Find the area of a circle:
(a) of radius (i) 5 cm   (ii) 8 cm
(b) of diameter (i) 6 cm   (ii) 16.4 cm.

10 Find the area of each of the following shapes.

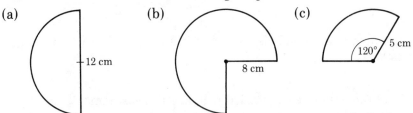

(a) 12 cm

(b) 8 cm

(c) 120° 5 cm

11 Water from a rotating spray falls over a circular area of radius 6 m. Calculate the area covered, correct to the nearest square metre.

12 Find the area of a gravel path, 1.2 m wide, that surrounds a circular flowerbed of radius 5.6 m.

13 What is the area of the largest circle that can be cut from a square sheet of paper with an area of 144 cm^2?

178

14 Find the area of each shaded region.

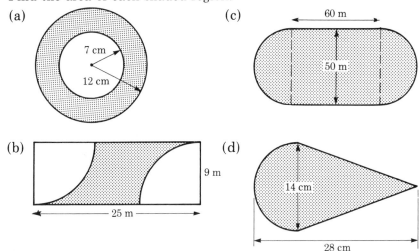

(a) 7 cm 12 cm

(c) 60 m 50 m

(b) 9 m 25 m

(d) 14 cm 28 cm

15 How many discs of diameter 6 cm can be stamped from a rectangular sheet of metal measuring 48 cm by 30 cm? What area of metal is wasted?

Exercise 65 Volume ═══════ AT **4** ═**4–7**

1 In this exercise give any answers that are not exact correct to three significant figures.

	Dimensions of cuboid			
	Length	Width	Height	Volume
(a)	12 cm	5 cm	3 cm	cm^3
(b)	46 cm	30 mm	45 mm	cm^3
(c)	8.6 m	450 cm	2.3 m	m^3
(d)	7.2 cm	3.9 cm	0.25 m	cm^3
(e)	10 cm		6 cm	480 cm^3
(f)		1.5 m	0.8 m	2.88 m^3

2 An open rectangular wooden box measures 21 cm × 11 cm × 7 cm. It is made from wood 0.5 cm thick. Find the capacity of the box.

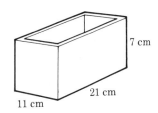

7 cm

21 cm

11 cm

179

3 Find the volume of each of the following prisms. You will probably find it useful to draw each cross-section.

(a)

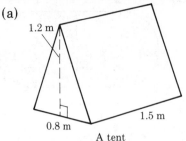

1.2 m
1.5 m
0.8 m
A tent

(d)

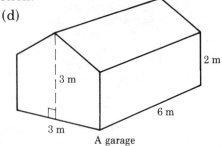

2 m
3 m
6 m
3 m
A garage

(b)

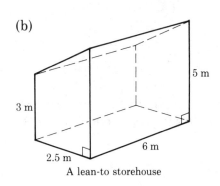

5 m
3 m
6 m
2.5 m
A lean-to storehouse

(e)

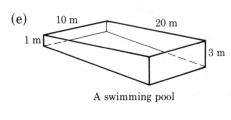

10 m
20 m
1 m
3 m
A swimming pool

(c)

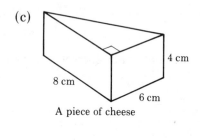

4 cm
8 cm
6 cm
A piece of cheese

(f)

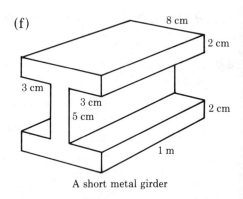

8 cm
2 cm
3 cm
3 cm
2 cm
5 cm
1 m
A short metal girder

4 Find the volume of each of the following cylinders:
(a) radius 3 cm, height 10 cm
(b) radius 8 cm, height 15 cm
(c) diameter 10 cm, height 12.5 cm
(d) diameter 9.4 cm, height 3.45 cm
(e) radius 0.4 m, height 1.56 m
(f) diameter 88 mm, height 12 mm.

5 Find the volume of each of the following solids. Use the π button on your calculator.

(a)

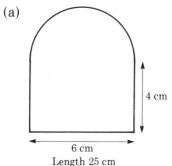

A metal disc 2 mm thick and 18 mm in diameter

(b)

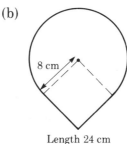

A metal tube 1 m long with internal and external diameters 10 mm and 12 mm

6 In this question the cross-sections of the solids and their lengths are given. Find their volumes.

(a)

4 cm

6 cm
Length 25 cm

(b)

8 cm

Length 24 cm

7 How many cylindrical cans of height 15 cm and diameter 10 cm can be filled from a full cylindrical tank of height 0.8 m and diameter 0.6 m?

8

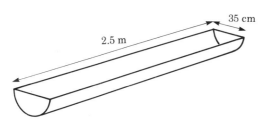

35 cm

2.5 m

A water trough is 2.5 m long and has a semi-circular cross-section of diameter 35 cm. How many litres of water does the trough hold when full?

9 A can of soup has a diameter of 7 cm and a height of 12 cm. The soup is poured into a cylindrical saucepan with a diameter of 12 cm. Find the depth of the soup in the saucepan.

10 A cube of metal of side 5 cm is melted down and recast, without any change of volume, into a cylinder of diameter 4 cm. How high is the cylinder?

Exercise 66 Accuracy and Calculations

AT **2** 3,6,7

1 Give each of the following lengths correct to the nearest metre:

(a) 5.8 m   (b) 8 m 77 cm   (c) 23.47 m   (d) 5928 cm.

2 Give each of the following lengths correct to two decimal places:

(a) 16.429 m   (b) 0.577 cm   (c) 4.025 m   (d) 0.098 mm.

3 Give each of the following areas correct to two significant figures:

(a) 24.95 cm^2 (b) 5287 m^2 (c) 342 cm^2 (d) 0.05666 m^2.

4 Give each of the following volumes correct to three significant figures:

(a) 6.927 cm^3 (b) 34592 m^3 (c) 1.0666 cm^3 (d) 0.03333 m^3.

5 The following distances are given correct to the nearest kilometre. Between what limits does each lie?

(a) 10 km   (b) 53 km   (c) 125 km   (d) 3 km

6 The following masses are given correct to the nearest kilogram. Between what limits does each lie?

(a) 2 kg   (b) 8 kg   (c) 17 kg   (d) 55 kg

7 The following numbers are given correct to two significant figures. Between what limits does each lie?

(a) 45   (b) 2700   (c) 0.73   (d) 8.2

8 The following numbers are given correct to two decimal places. Between what limits does each lie?

(a) 4.27   (b) 18.92   (c) 0.53   (d) 0.07

9 Between what limits does each of the following measurements lie?

(a) 50 cm, to the nearest 10 centimetres.
(b) 50 cm, to the nearest centimetre.
(c) 50 cm to the nearest tenth of a centimetre.

10 The altitude of an aircraft is displayed to passengers as 10 000 m, correct to the nearest 500 m. What are the greatest and least possible heights of the aircraft?

11 A signpost reads Redwood 20 km. Two hundred metres nearer Redwood another signpost reads Redwood 19 km. Explain this apparent contradiction.

182

12 The length of each of the sides of a square, correct to the nearest centimetre, is 5 cm.

(a) Write down the limits between which the actual measurement lies.

(b) What are the greatest and least possible perimeters?

(c) What are the greatest and least possible areas?

13 The dimensions of a rectangle are recorded as 12 cm by 10 cm, each correct to the nearest centimetre.

(a) Write down the limits between which each measurement lies.

(b) Find the greatest and least possible perimeters.

(c) Find the greatest and least possible areas.

14 Repeat question 13 for a rectangle measuring 50 cm by 40 cm, each correct to the nearest 10 centimetres.

15 The dimensions of a cubical box are 12 cm by 10 cm by 6 cm, each measurement being correct to the nearest centimetre.

(a) Write down the limits between which each measurement lies.

(b) Hence find:
  (i) the greatest and least possible areas of the largest faces of the box
  (ii) the greatest and least possible volumes. Give each volume correct to the nearest cubic centimetre.

(c) Express the difference in these volumes as a percentage of the smaller volume.

Exercise 67 Polygons ══════AT4═ 6

1 In each case find the size of the angle marked x.

(a)

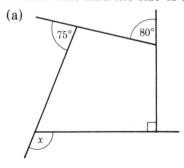

(b)

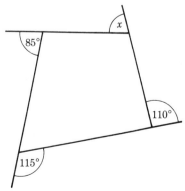

(c)

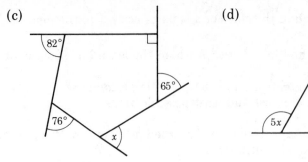

(d)

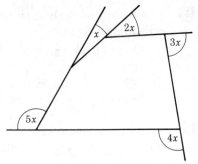

2 Find the size of each exterior angle of a regular polygon with:
(a) 12 sides   (b) 10 sides   (c) 18 sides   (d) 20 sides.

3 Find the size of each interior angle of a regular polygon with:
(a) 8 sides   (b) 9 sides   (c) 24 sides   (d) 15 sides.

4 In each case find the size of the angle(s) marked x.

(a)

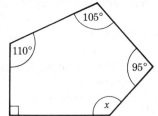

(c)

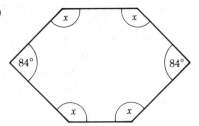

(b)

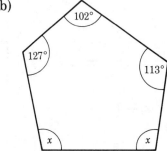

(d)

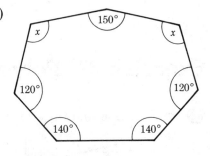

5 How many sides has a regular polygon if each exterior angle is:
(a) 45°   (b) 15°   (c) 12°.

6 How many sides has a regular polygon if each interior angle is:
(a) 150°   (b) 160°   (c) 156°.

7 A hexagon has five exterior angles of 63°. Calculate the size of the sixth exterior angle.

8 A pentagon has three exterior angles of 82°. The other two exterior angles are equal. Find the size of each.

9 Is it possible to have a regular polygon with exterior angles of the following sizes? For those that are possible, give the number of sides.

(a) 40°   (b) 50°   (c) 60°   (d) 70°

10 Is it possible to have a regular polygon with interior angles of the following sizes? For those that are possible, give the number of sides.

(a) 145°   (b) 135°   (c) 125°   (d) 165°

11

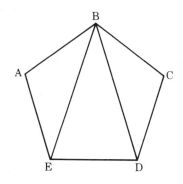

ABCDE is a regular pentagon. Find the sizes of the angles in △BED.

12

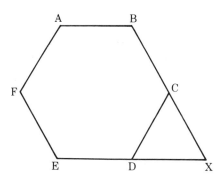

The sides BC and ED of a regular hexagon ABCDEF are produced to meet at X. Find the angles in △CXD.

13 ABCDEF is a regular hexagon. Calculate the angles in △ABE.

14 In an octagon each angle except one is 10° greater than the angle next to it in a clockwise direction. Find the size of: (a) the smallest angle (b) the largest angle.

185

Exercise 68 Probability ═══ AT **5** ═ 4-8

1 Sid rolls a dice. What is the probability that he scores:

(a) 5   (b) 1   (c) 0   (d) 7.

2 Antonia draws a card from an ordinary pack of 52 playing cards. What is the probability that the card she draws is:

(a) a black card   (c) a ten
(b) a diamond   (d) the ace of clubs?

3 What is the probability of throwing 3 or higher with a dice?

4 One letter is chosen at random from the letters in the word AUTOMOBILE. What is the probability that it is:

(a) the letter O   (d) a consonant
(b) a vowel   (e) a letter that has both line and
(c) the letter L   rotational symmetry?

5 A bag holds three blue counters, two black counters and five white counters. One counter is drawn at random from the bag. What is the probability that it is

(a) a black counter
(b) a white counter
(c) not a blue counter?

6 A book of 120 pages has at least one picture on each of 75 pages. If one page is chosen at random, what is the probability that:

(a) it has a picture on it
(b) it does not have a picture on it?

7 A roulette wheel is spun. What is the probability that when it stops it will be pointing to:

(a) an even number
(b) a number less than 15, excluding zero
(c) a multiple of 5
(d) a prime number?

(The numbers on a roulette wheel go from 0 to 35. Zero is neither even nor odd.)

8 In a raffle to raise money for Age Concern, 400 tickets are sold.

(a) If you buy five tickets, what is the probability that:
    (i) you will win first prize
    (ii) you will not win first prize?

186

(b) How many tickets should you buy to make certain of winning first prize?

9 Two ordinary six-sided dice are rolled. Draw up a possibility space showing all the possible combinations in which the dice may stop. Use this possibility space to find the probability that the total score is:

(a) 5 or less
(b) a double
(c) more than 6
(d) at least 8.

10 One box contains three CDs and two tapes. A second box contains one CD and three tapes. Draw a possibility space showing the various ways in which you could select one item from each box. Use this possibility space to find the probability that:

(a) both items are CDs
(b) both items are tapes.

Exercise 69 Travel Graphs ══AT **3** ══ 7

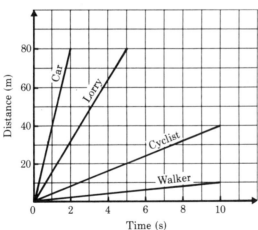

Use these distance–time graphs to answer the questions that follow.

(a) How far does the walker go in 10 seconds? What is his speed in m/s?

(b) Use the graphs to find the speed, in m/s, of:
   (i) the cyclist   (ii) the lorry   (iii) the car.

(c) Find in kilometres per hour:
   (i) the speed of the cyclist   (ii) the speed of the lorry.

(d) Convert each speed into miles per hour
   (assume that 8 km = 5 miles).

187

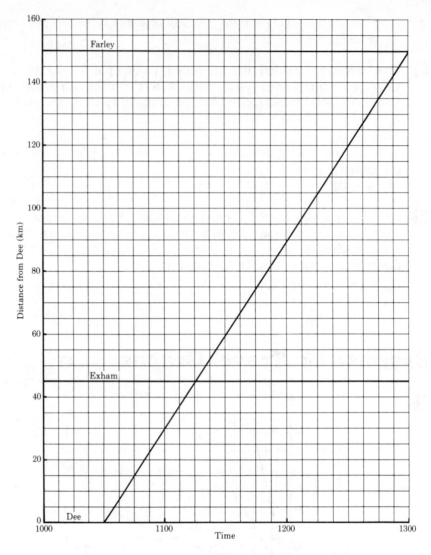

The graph shows the journey of a car through three towns, Dee, Exham and Farley, that lie on a straight road. Use the graph to answer the following questions.

(a) How far is it from:
    (i) Dee to Exham
    (ii) Exham to Farley?

(b) At what time does the car:
    (i) leave Dee
    (ii) pass through Exham
    (iii) arrive at Farley?

(c) How long does the whole journey take?

(d) What is the average speed of the car for the whole journey?

3 The graph represents the journey of a motorist from Oxford to Birmingham and back.

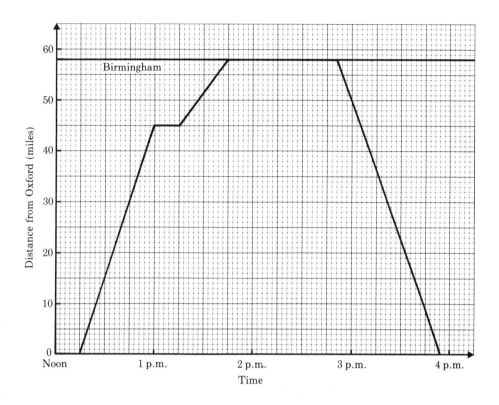

Use the graph to find:

(a) the distance between the two cities

(b) the time at which the motorist:
   (i) left Oxford

   (ii) arrived in Birmingham

   (iii) left Birmingham

   (iv) got back to Oxford

(c) how long a break she took on the outward journey

(d) her average speed
   (i) before the break

   (ii) for the outward journey

   (iii) for the return journey.

4 The graph shows the journey of two canal boats, A and B. Boat A travels upstream from Axen to Banton, passing through two locks on the way.

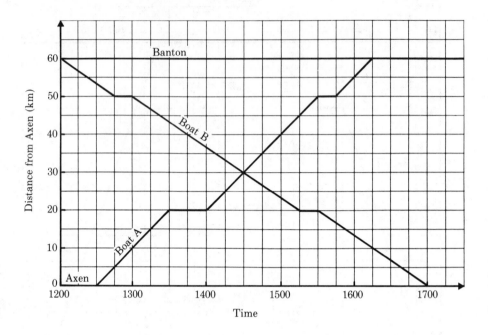

(a) How far is it from Axen:
   (i) to the first lock
   (ii) to the second lock?

(b) At what time did Boat A:
   (i) leave Axen
   (ii) enter the first lock
   (iii) leave the second lock
   (iv) arrive at Banton?

(c) Is Boat B travelling upstream or downstream?

(d) At what time did Boat B:
   (i) start its journey
   (ii) complete its journey?

(e) How long did each boat spend in locks?

(f) At what speed did each boat travel?

(g) When and where did the two boats pass?

(h) What was Boat B's average speed for the whole journey?

Exercise 70 Function Machines

In questions 1 to 6 copy the tables and use the function machines to complete them.

1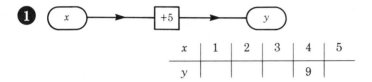

x	1	2	3	4	5
y				9	

2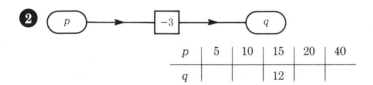

p	5	10	15	20	40
q			12		

3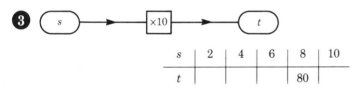

s	2	4	6	8	10
t				80	

(a) What is t when s is 7?
(b) What is t when s is 15?

4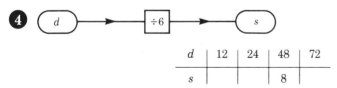

d	12	24	48	72
s			8	

(a) What is s when d is 36?
(b) What is s when d is 84?

5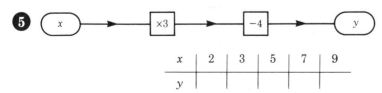

x	2	3	5	7	9
y					

(a) What is y when x is 6?
(b) What is y when x is 8?

191

6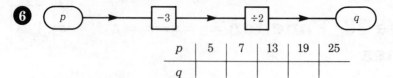

p	5	7	13	19	25
q					

(a) What is q when p is 21?
(b) What is q when p is 9?

7 Look at this table.

x	1	2	4	8	16
y	3	5	9	17	33

(a) The next number in the top row is 32. What is the value of y below it?
(b) What is y when x is 5?
(c) What is y when x is 19?
(d) Make a function machine for this table:

8 Study this table.

s	1	2	3	4	5
d	3	8	13	18	23

(a) What is d if s = 6?
(b) What is d if s = 9?
(c) Make a function machine for this table.

In questions 9 to 14 write each function machine as a formula.

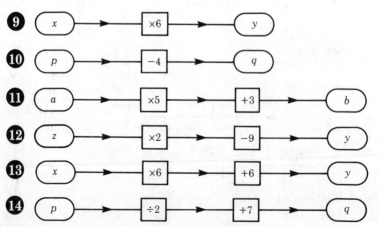

9 x → ×6 → y

10 p → −4 → q

11 a → ×5 → +3 → b

12 z → ×2 → −9 → y

13 x → ×6 → +6 → y

14 p → ÷2 → +7 → q

192

Exercise 71 Networks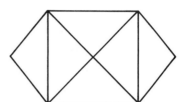

A network is traversable if it is possible to go over every line exactly once without taking the pencil off the paper. In questions 1 to 12 copy each network and say whether or not it is traversable. Do you end up at your starting point?

1

6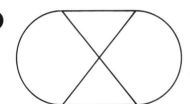

2

7

3

8

4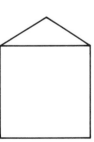

9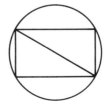

5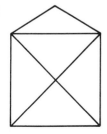

10

193

11

 12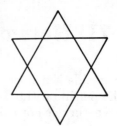

13 Can you draw a network of your own:
(a) that is traversable
(b) that is not traversable?

14

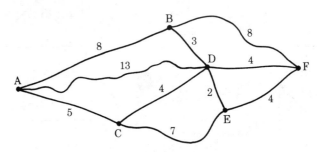

The diagram above is a simplified map showing the distances (in kilometres) between a group of villages lettered A to F.

(a) What is the shortest route from A to F.
(b) Is it possible to start at A, visit every other village, and return to A without travelling along any road twice?
(c) Is it possible to start at A, travel along every road exactly once, and end up at A?

15

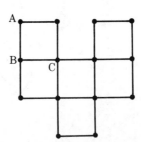

The diagram shows part of the road layout in an American town. Post Office collection boxes are placed at every road intersection and the distance between any two adjacent boxes is 100 m.

(a) Is it possible to start at A or B or C and cover the complete road system without driving along any road more than once?
(b) Starting at B what is the shortest distance that a van can travel to visit every box and return to B? Does the van have to pass any box more than once to make this shortest trip?

Exercise 72 Linear Equations

Solve the following equations.

1 $x + 5 = 9$

2 $x + 4 = 17$

3 $10 + x = 21$

4 $4 + y = 9$

5 $z + 4 = 9$

6 $a + 7 = 10$

7 $b + 11 = 12$

8 $8 + c = 14$

9 $a + 1 = 8$

10 $b + 3 = 5$

11 $9 + a = 12$

12 $12 + b = 15$

13 $x - 3 = 4$

14 $x - 7 = 10$

15 $x - 4 = 3$

16 $x - 10 = 2$

17 $a - 8 = 3$

18 $b - 5 = 7$

19 $y - 2 = 1$

20 $z - 9 = 9$

21 $a - 3 = 3$

22 $b - 10 = 1$

23 $y - 3 = 1$

24 $z - 5 = 7$

25 $5 = x + 2$

26 $7 = x + 1$

27 $3 = x - 4$

28 $8 = x - 5$

29 $3 = y - 2$

30 $5 = z - 5$

31 $10 = y + 7$

32 $8 = z + 3$

33 $x + 4 = 7$

34 $x - 4 = 7$

35 $x - 7 = 4$

36 $14 = x - 7$

37 $x + 7 = 3$

38 $x + 9 = 6$

39 $5 = x + 7$

40 $8 = x + 2$

41 $x - 3 = 6$

42 $x + 3 = 6$

43 $x + 6 = 3$

44 $x - 6 = 3$

45 $3x = 12$

46 $2x = 2$

47 $6a = 7$

48 $5a = 3$

49 $5x + 3 = 13$

50 $3x + 5 = 14$

51 $15 = 7x + 1$

52 $3z + 7 = 10$

53 $9x + 2 = 20$

54 $12 = 7a + 5$

55 $5a - 3 = 17$

56 $4x - 5 = 3$

57 $2x - 3 = 4$

58 $4x + 3 = -5$

59 $3a + 1 = 11$

60 $15 = 7z - 2$

61 $5x + 1 = 4x + 7$ **65** $6x + 8 = 3x + 5$ **69** $7 - 3x = -7 + 4x$

62 $2x + 7 = 3x + 1$ **66** $7x - 3 = 5x + 3$ **70** $30 - 7x = 10 + 3x$

63 $3x - 2 = 5x - 12$ **67** $3x - 5 = 11 - x$ **71** $22 - 4x = 10 + 2x$

64 $4z + 9 = 7z + 18$ **68** $7 + x = 13 - 5x$ **72** $16 - 5x = 2x + 2$

Exercise 73 Substituting into Formulae

AT**2** 7,8

AT**3** 5

1 Given that $v = u + at$, find v when $u = 30$, $a = 10$ and $t = 4$.

2 Given that $a = bc - 2d$, find a when $b = 4$, $c = 3$ and $d = 6$.

3 If $s = \frac{1}{2}(a + b + c)$, find s when $a = 5$, $b = 9$ and $c = 10$.

4 If $s = vt$, find s when $v = 40$ and $t = 2.5$.

5 If $a = \frac{bc}{d}$, find a when $b = 6$, $c = 9$ and $d = 18$.

6 Given that $s = \frac{p + q}{r}$, find s when $p = 3.5$, $q = 10.5$ and $r = 7$.

7 Given that $a = \frac{2b - c}{d}$, find a when $b = 7$, $c = 8$ and $d = 3$.

8 If $a = \frac{1}{b} + \frac{1}{c}$, find a when $b = 6$ and $c = 3$.

9 If $A = \left(\frac{a + b}{2}\right)h$, find A when $a = 7$, $b = 9$ and $h = 6$.

10 If $x + y + z = 180$, find x when $y = 47$ and $z = 95$.

11 If $T = (n - 2)180$, find T when $n = 7$.

12 Given that $I = \frac{PRT}{100}$, find I when $P = 700$, $R = 4$ and $T = 5$.

13 Given that $x = \dfrac{a + b + c + d}{4}$, find x when $a = 8$, $b = 15$, $c = 23$ and $d = 14$.

14 Given that $A = a^2 + ab$, find A when $a = 5$ and $b = 7$.

15 Given that $y = \frac{1}{2}x + 5$, find y when
(a) $x = 8$
(b) $x = 5$
(c) $x = -3$.

16 If $y = mx + c$, find y when $m = 3$, $x = 2$ and $c = -3$.

17 If $y = x^2 + 3x + 4$, find y when $x = 4$.

18 If $y = x^2 - 7x + 6$, find y when $x = -3$.

19 If $y = 2x^2 + 3x - 5$, find y when $x = 4$.

20 If $y = 3x^2 - 6x + 1$, find y when $x = -2$.

21 Given that $R = p^2 + q^2$, find R when $p = 3$ and $q = 6$.

22 Given that $V = 4x^2y$, find V when $x = 6$ and $y = 5$.

23 Given that $\dfrac{a}{b} = \dfrac{x}{y}$, find a when $x = 9$, $y = 15$ and $b = 5$.

24 Given that $\dfrac{1}{a} = \dfrac{1}{b} + \dfrac{1}{c}$, find:
(a) a when $b = 4$ and $c = 2$
(b) a when $b = 2$ and $c = 3$
(c) b when $a = 2$ and $c = 4$

25 If $v^2 = u^2 + 2as$, find:
(a) v when $u = 4$, $a = \frac{1}{2}$ and $s = 9$
(b) a when $v = 7$, $u = 5$ and $s = 6$.

26 If $R = \dfrac{12}{i}$, find:
(a) R when $i = 3$
(a) i when $R = 6$
(a) R when $i = 2.5$

Exercise 74 Statistics 2 ═══════AT**5**═5-7

1 This is a list of the heights (each to the nearest centimetre) of sixty-five pupils.

145	144	152	148	151	147	142	145	150	142	138	153	146
147	160	153	142	136	150	146	147	157	152	164	142	148
142	149	143	148	142	158	143	137	163	153	142	158	145
145	140	149	135	147	151	142	154	139	159	146	138	158
146	138	154	160	143	159	149	144	160	148	145	154	144

(a) What is the height of the shortest pupil?

(b) How many pupils were shorter than 145 cm?

(c) Copy and complete this frequency table.

Height, h, in cm	Frequency
$135 \leqslant h < 140$	
$140 \leqslant h < 145$	
$145 \leqslant h < 150$	
$150 \leqslant h < 155$	
$155 \leqslant h < 160$	
$160 \leqslant h < 165$	

(d) How many pupils have a height of 150 cm or more?

(e) Draw a bar chart to illustrate this information.

2 The table records the means of transport for coming to school on a given day for a group of school children.

Means of transport	On foot	Bus	Car	Bicycle	Other
Frequency	12	8	9	4	3

(a) How many pupils are there in the group?

(b) Draw a pie chart to represent this information.
    (Use a circle with a diameter of at least 4 cm.)

3 The population of a country was divided into groups according to age. The results are given in the table.

Age-group	Under 10	10–19	20–39	40–59	60–79	80+
Number of people in millions (frequency)	3	3	5	6	4	3

(a) What is the total population?

(b) Draw a pie chart to represent this age distribution.

198

4 The table below gives the history and geography marks for each of fifteen pupils in end of term tests.

History	45	56	82	50	36	88	62	52	73	84	86	38	48	56	47
Geography	54	47	65	72	50	72	65	40	85	72	78	52	61	55	55

(a) Show this information on a graph. Use 1 cm to represent 5 marks on each axis. Mark the horizontal axis from 35 to 90 for history and the vertical axis from 40 to 90 for geography.

(b) Phyllis is good at history. Is she likely to be good at geography?

5 The table gives the French mark and the physics mark for each of ten pupils in a mid-term examination.

French	5	8	3	10	16	12	8	8	18	15
Physics	14	10	15	10	8	9	9	11	6	8

(a) Show this information on a graph. Use 1 cm to represent 2 marks on each axis.

(b) Svenga is good at French. Is she likely to be good at physics?

6 The table gives the maths marks and the history marks of eighteen third-year pupils.

Maths	38	42	45	45	49	50	54	55	56	58	64	68	72	84	92	93	96	96
History	45	60	52	54	63	55	58	59	62	64	58	72	66	65	70	85	92	74

(a) Show this information on a scatter graph. Use a scale of 1 cm for 5 marks on each axis, scaling the horizontal axis from 30 to 100 for maths and the vertical axis from 40 to 100 for history.

(b) Sarah is good at history. Is she likely to be good at maths?

(c) Draw the line of best fit to represent this data. How would you describe the correlation: 'weak', 'moderate' or 'strong'?

7 It has been suggested that height and armspan (the distance from finger tip to finger tip when the arms are outstretched) have a strong correlation. The heights and armspans of twelve teenagers are given in the table.

Height (cm)	146	158	172	175	189	163	183	168	184	164	180	156
Armspan (cm)	147	160	169	178	189	162	185	171	180	163	178	155

(a) Show this information on a scatter graph. Use a scale of 4 cm to represent 10 cm on each axis, scaling each axis from 140 to 180. (Plot height on the horizontal axis and armspan on the vertical axis.)

(b) Draw the line of best fit to represent this data.

(c) Would you agree with the statement that 'a person's armspan is a good indication of their height'?

(d) Steve has an armspan of 165 cm. Estimate his height.

Exercise 75 Enlargements ═══AT4═6,7

In questions 1 to 6 copy each diagram on to squared paper using 1 cm as 1 unit. △A′B′C′ is the image of △ABC under an enlargement. By drawing suitable straight lines find, for each diagram:

(a) the coordinates of the centre of enlargement
(b) the scale factor.

1

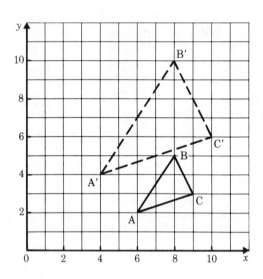

2

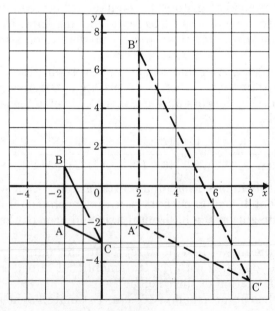

200

3

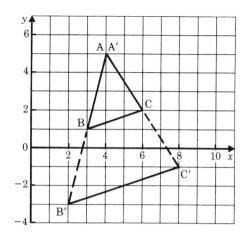

4

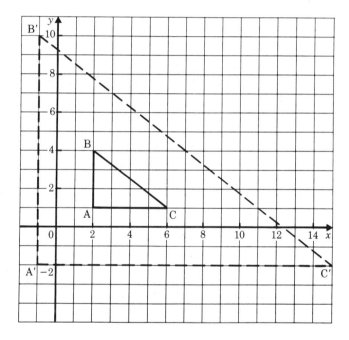

5

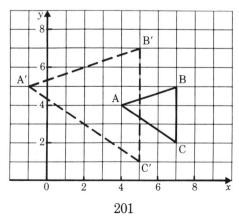

6

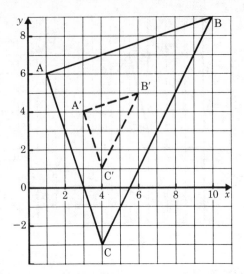

In questions 7 to 10 copy the diagram on to squared paper using 1 cm as 1 unit. If P is the centre of enlargement, draw the image of △ABC under the given enlargement. Label it A′B′C′.

7

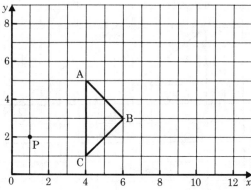

Scale factor 2

8

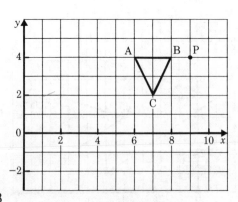

Scale factor 3

9

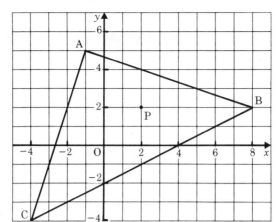

Scale factor $\frac{1}{3}$

10

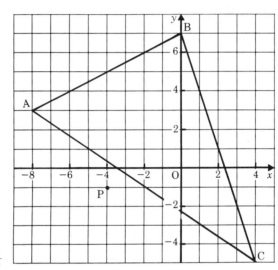

Scale factor $\frac{3}{4}$

11 Draw x and y axes and label each from 1 to 10, using 1 cm as 1 unit on both axes. Plot the points A(3, 3), B(7, 4) and C(6, 1). Find the image of $\triangle ABC$ under an enlargement with centre P(6, 0) and scale factor 2. Label the image A'B'C'.

12 Draw x and y axes scaling the x-axis from -2 to 10 and the y-axis from -5 to 5. Use 1 cm as 1 unit on both axes. Plot the points A(3, 2), B(5, 2) and C(5, -4). Find the image of $\triangle ABC$ under an enlargement with centre (-1, -2) and scale factor $1\frac{1}{2}$. Label the image A'B'C'.

13 Draw axes for x and y and label each from 0 to 10 using 1 cm as 1 unit on both axes. Plot the points A(0, 6), B(9, 9) and C(6, 3). Find the image of $\triangle ABC$ under an enlargement with centre (6, 6) and scale factor $\frac{1}{3}$. Label the image A'B'C'.

203

Exercise 76 Similar Triangles

1 In triangles ABC and DEF, $\hat{A} = \hat{E}$ and $\hat{B} = \hat{D}$.

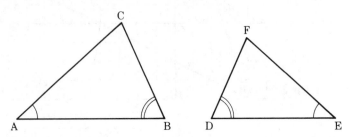

If AB = 5 cm, AC = 4 cm and EF = 6 cm, find the length of DE.

2 In triangles ABC and DEF, $\hat{A} = \hat{P}$ and $\hat{B} = \hat{Q}$.

If AC = 10 cm, PR = 12 cm and QR = 10 cm, find the length of BC.

3

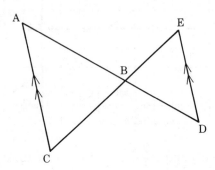

(a) Show that triangles ABC and DBE are similar.
(b) If AB = 5 cm, BC = 5 cm, AC = 6 cm and BD = 4 cm, find the lengths of BE and ED.

4 Find the length of XY.

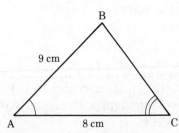

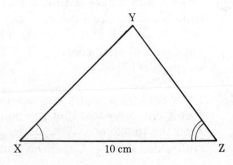

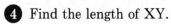

5 State whether the following pairs of triangles are similar. In each case say which angle, if any, is equal to $\hat{A}$.

(a)

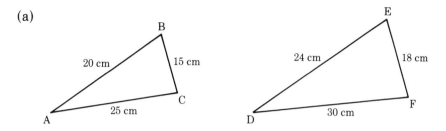

(b)

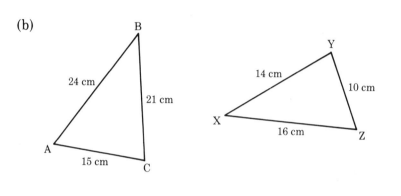

(c)

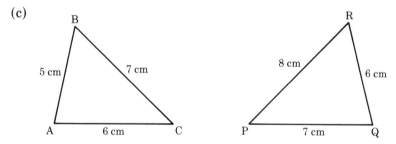

6 State whether the following pairs of triangles are similar. If they are, find the missing lengths.

(a)

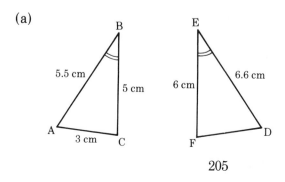

(b)

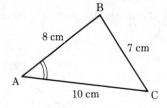

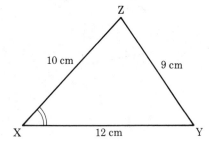

(c)

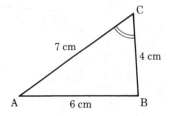

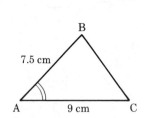

(d)

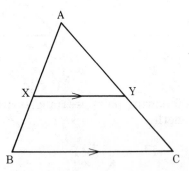

7

(a) If AB = 5 cm, AX = 3 cm and AC = 7.5 cm, find the length of AY.

(b) If AB = 14 cm, AX = 8 cm, AY = 5 cm and XY = 7 cm, find the lengths of AC and BC.

(c) If BX = 4 cm, AY = 9 cm, AC = 12 cm and BC = 20 cm find the lengths of AX, AB and XY.

8

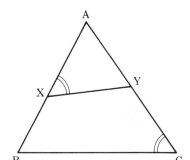

X and Y are points on the sides AB and AC of a triangle ABC such that $A\hat{X}Y = A\hat{C}B$.

(a) Given that AB = 35 cm, BC = 25 cm, AC = 30 cm and XY = 15 cm, find the lengths of AX and AY.

(b) Given that AB = 15 cm, AC = 10 cm, XY = 8.4 cm and AX = 7 cm, find the lengths of BC and AY.

9

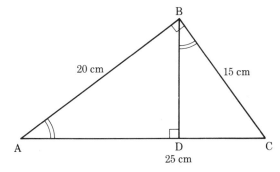

ABC is a right-angled triangle and D is the foot of the perpendicular from B to AC.

(a) Use the information in the diagram to prove that triangles ABC and ABD are similar.

Complete the ratios: $\dfrac{AB}{AD} = \dfrac{BC}{} = \dfrac{}{AB}$

Hence find the length of DB.

(b) Prove that triangles ABD and BDC are similar.

Complete the ratios: $\dfrac{AB}{BC} = \dfrac{AD}{} = \dfrac{}{DC}$

Hence find the lengths of AD and DC.

10

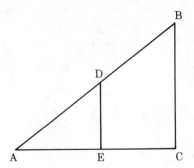

The diagram represents a roof AB, joined at the top to a vertical wall BC and supported by a strut DE. If the height of the support is 2.4 m, the height of the wall is 6.6 m and the bottom of the roof is 2 m from the support, find the distance from the support to the wall.

Exercise 77 Index Numbers $=\dfrac{AT\,2}{AT\,3}$ ⬚5⧄7

1 Write in index form:
  (a) $5 \times 5 \times 5$
  (b) $3 \times 3 \times 3 \times 3$
  (c) $2 \times 2 \times 2 \times 2 \times 2$
  (d) $9 \times 9 \times 9$
  (e) 4×4
  (f) $8 \times 8 \times 8 \times 8 \times 8$

2 Find the value of:
  (a) $2 \times 2 \times 2 \times 2$
  (b) $5 \times 5 \times 5$
  (c) $10 \times 10 \times 10 \times 10$

3 Find the value of:
  (a) 2^3
  (b) 2^6
  (c) 3^3
  (d) 8^2
  (e) 10^5
  (f) 5^4

4 Copy and complete this table.

3^1	3^2	3^3	3^4	3^5	3^6
3			81		

5 Write 100, 1000, 10 000 and 1 000 000 as powers of 10.

6 Write out the correct statement from each of the following pairs.
  (a) $2^3 = 6$ or $2^3 = 8$
  (b) $10 + 10 + 10 = 10 \times 3$ or $10 \times 10 \times 10 = 10 \times 3$
  (c) $3^5 = 243$ or $3^5 = 729$

7 Write as a single expression in index form:

(a) $3^3 \times 3^2$ (c) $7^2 \times 7^2$ (e) $3 \times 3^5 \times 3^2$

(b) $2^5 \times 2^2$ (d) $5^4 \times 5^3$ (f) $2^2 \times 2^3 \times 2^5$

8 Find the value of:

(a) 3×2^3 (c) $2^3 \times 3^2$ (e) 5×10^3

(b) 4×3^2 (d) $3^3 \times 2^2$ (f) 8×10^5

9 Find the value of:

(a) 7.5×10^3 (c) 3.6×10^5 (e) 4.4×10^1

(b) 1.9×10^2 (d) 8.3×10^4 (f) 5.8×10^6

10 Find the value of:

(a) 6.24×10^3 (c) 26.3×10^5 (e) 8.152×10^2

(b) 4.92×10^1 (d) 147×10^4 (f) 3.095×10^6

11 Express each of the following numbers as the product of prime factors in index form:

(a) 120   (c) 720   (e) 6125

(b) 189   (d) 784   (f) 31 850

12 Find the value of:

(a) 2^{-3} (c) 7^{-1} (e) 4^{-4}

(b) 3^{-3} (d) 5^{-2} (f) 10^{-2}

13 Find the value of:

(a) 2.2×10^{-2} (c) 8.21×10^{-3} (e) 4.652×10^{-3}

(b) 5.7×10^{-4} (d) 6.92×10^{-5} (f) 3.005×10^{-2}

14 Write as a single number in index form:

(a) $3^2 \div 3^5$ (c) $5 \div 5^3$ (e) $3^4 \div 3^5 \times 3^3$

(b) $2^4 \div 2^7$ (d) $10^2 \div 10^6$ (f) $2^3 \times 2^4 \div 2^9$

15 Find the value of:

(a) 2^0 (c) $3^3 \times 5^0$ (c) $5^3 \div 5^3$

(b) 3^0 (d) $4^0 \times 7^2$ (f) $\left(\frac{1}{2}\right)^{-2}$

16 Find the value of:

(a) $\dfrac{2^3 + 3^3}{5}$ (b) $\dfrac{5^2 - 2^4}{3^2}$ (c) $\dfrac{2^3 + 3^2}{2^5 - 2^4 - 2^0}$

17 Find the value of:

(a) $2^{-2} + 3^{-1}$ (b) $2^2 \times 3^{-2}$ (c) $3^{-3} \div 2^{-4}$

Exercise 78 Standard Form

1 The following numbers are given in standard form. Write them as ordinary numbers.

(a) 2.4×10^3

(b) 8×10^5

(c) 7.6×10^{10}

(d) 3.72×10^4

(e) 5.902×10^6

(f) 5.8×10^{-2}

(g) 8.64×10^{-3}

(h) 4.05×10^{-5}

(i) 1.92×10^{-4}

2 Write the following numbers in standard form:

(a) 360

(b) 4200

(c) 64 900

(d) 0.07

(e) 0.083

(f) 0.0042

(g) 5000

(h) 920 000

(i) 0.000 006

3 Given below are several readings from the display of my calculator. Write each display as an ordinary number

(a) | 7.3   −08 |

(b) | 1.8   05 |

(c) | 6.5   −10 |

(d) | 4.9   11 |

4 The distance of the Earth from the Sun is approximately 93 million miles. Write this distance in standard form.

5 The average distance of Mercury from the Sun is about twenty-nine million miles. Write this distance in standard form.

6 Neptune's mean distance from the Sun is 2793 million miles. Write this number in standard form.

7 Saturn's mean distance from the Sun is about 9×10^8 miles. How many million miles is this?

8 The mean distance of the planet Uranus from the Sun is about 2.9×10^6 kilometres. How many million kilometres is this?

9 If $a = 8 \times 10^2$ and $b = 4 \times 10^3$, find as an ordinary number:

(a) $a + b$

(b) ab

(c) $b - a$

(d) $\dfrac{b}{a}$

10 If $a = 3.2 \times 10^6$ and $b = 4 \times 10^4$, find in standard form:

(a) $a + b$

(b) $a - b$

(c) ab

(d) $\dfrac{a}{b}$

11 If $p = 3.5 \times 10^{-2}$ and $q = 5.5 \times 10^{-3}$, find as an ordinary number:

(a) $p + q$ (b) $p - q$ (c) $p + 10q$ (d) $3p + 4q$

12 If $x = 7.2 \times 10^{-3}$ and $y = 2.4 \times 10^{-4}$, find in standard form:

(a) $x + y$ (b) $x - y$ (c) $\dfrac{x}{y}$ (d) $x + 5y$

Exercise 79 Vectors ═══════════ AT **4** = 8

1 In each part (a) to (f) a vector is given followed by the coordinates of its starting point. Find the coordinates of its finishing point.

(a) $\begin{pmatrix} 4 \\ 2 \end{pmatrix}$, (3, 2)   (d) $\begin{pmatrix} 2 \\ -3 \end{pmatrix}$, (3, −7)

(b) $\begin{pmatrix} 5 \\ 1 \end{pmatrix}$, (−4, 1)   (e) $\begin{pmatrix} 3 \\ 6 \end{pmatrix}$, (−4, −2)

(c) $\begin{pmatrix} -4 \\ 6 \end{pmatrix}$, (2, 6)   (f) $\begin{pmatrix} -3 \\ -5 \end{pmatrix}$, (−2, −4)

2 (a) If $\overrightarrow{AB} = \begin{pmatrix} 3 \\ 5 \end{pmatrix}$ and B has coordinates (2, 2), write down the coordinates of A.

(b) If $\overrightarrow{BC} = \begin{pmatrix} -2 \\ 4 \end{pmatrix}$ and C has coordinates (3, −2), write down the coordinates of B.

3 Write down the vector $\overrightarrow{XY}$ if:

(a) X is the point (2, 6) and Y is the point (4, 9)
(b) X is the point (−5, 1) and Y is the point (2, 6)
(c) X is the point (4, 1) and Y is the point (2, 7)
(d) X is the point (8, 2) and Y is the point (5, −3).

4 If $\mathbf{a} = \begin{pmatrix} 2 \\ 5 \end{pmatrix}$ and $\mathbf{b} = \begin{pmatrix} 6 \\ -4 \end{pmatrix}$ draw diagrams to represent:

(a) $2\mathbf{a}$ (b) $-\mathbf{a}$ (c) $\frac{1}{2}\mathbf{b}$ (d) $-2\mathbf{b}$ (e) $\mathbf{a} + \mathbf{b}$

5 If $\mathbf{a} = \begin{pmatrix} 4 \\ 3 \end{pmatrix}$, $\mathbf{b} = \begin{pmatrix} 3 \\ 7 \end{pmatrix}$ and $\mathbf{c} = \begin{pmatrix} -2 \\ -3 \end{pmatrix}$ find

(a) $\mathbf{a} - \mathbf{b}$ (b) $\mathbf{b} - \mathbf{c}$ (c) $\mathbf{a} + \mathbf{b} + \mathbf{c}$
(d) $2\mathbf{a} - 3\mathbf{b}$ (c) $\mathbf{a} - 2\mathbf{b} + 3\mathbf{c}$ (f) $3\mathbf{a} - 2\mathbf{c}$

211

6 Find the image of the point (4, 5) under the translation described by the vector $\begin{pmatrix} -2 \\ 3 \end{pmatrix}$.

7 Find the vector that maps the point (3, 1) to the point (5, 6).

8 Find the point that is mapped to the point (2, 6) under a translation described by the vector $\begin{pmatrix} 3 \\ -5 \end{pmatrix}$.

9 A is the point (−2, −1), B is the point (2, 3) and $\overrightarrow{BC} = \begin{pmatrix} 3 \\ -2 \end{pmatrix}$. Find:

(a) $\overrightarrow{AB}$ (b) the coordinates of C   (c) $\overrightarrow{CA}$.

10

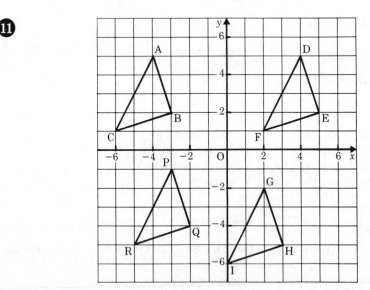

Give the vectors describing the translations that map:
(a) ABCD to PQRS   (b) PQRS to WXYZ.

11

Give the vectors describing the translations that map:
(a) △ABC to △DEF   (c) △PQR to △DEF
(b) △ABC to △GHI   (d) △DEF to △ABC.

212

Exercise 80 Constructing Formulae

1 In each case, write down a formula connecting the given letters.

(a) A number x is equal to the sum of two numbers a and b.

(b) A number a is equal to the product of two numbers b and c.

(c) A number z is equal to four times the product of two numbers x and y.

(d) A number a is equal to half the sum of two numbers b and c.

(e) A number z is equal to the sum of two numbers a and b divided by a number c.

In each question from 2 to 5, write down a formula connecting the given letters.

2 A number p is equal to the square of a number q plus a number r.

3 A number u is equal to a number v from which is subtracted the product of two numbers a and t.

4 A number E is equal to a number R multiplied by the square of a number i.

5 A number A is equal to a number π multiplied by the square of a number R.

6 Grapefruit cost x pence each. How much will n grapefruit cost? Give your answer:

(a) in pence (b) in pounds.

7 A car travels v miles in one hour. If it covers s miles in t hours, find a formula connecting v, s and t.

8 The perimeter of a square with a side of length x cm is P cm and its area is A cm^2. Find a formula connecting:

(a) P and x (b) A and x (c) A and P.

9 A rectangle is a cm long, b cm wide and has a perimeter of P cm. Find:

(a) a formula for P in terms of a and b

(b) a formula for a in terms of P and b.

10 Apples are sold at a pence each. I can buy x apples for £P. Find a formula for P in terms of a and x.

11 Lynn's purse contains x ten-pence coins and y fifty-pence coins. The total value of these coins is £z. Find a formula for z in terms of x and y.

12 Sandra buys x oranges at p pence each and y grapefruit at q pence each. In all she spends £z. Find a formula for z in terms of the other letters.

Exercise 81 Simultaneous ══AT**3**═ 7
Linear Equations

Solve the following pairs of equations.

1 $x + y = 9$
$x - y = 5$

6 $4x + y = 14$
$3x - y = 7$

2 $4x + y = 14$
$2x + y = 8$

7 $x + 5y = 17$
$3x - 5y = 11$

3 $3x + y = 13$
$5x + y = 19$

8 $6p - q = 25$
$6p + 3q = 21$

4 $3x + 2y = 11$
$x + 2y = 1$

9 $5x - 2y = 19$
$x + 2y = -1$

5 $5x + 3y = 7$
$5x + y = 9$

10 $4x - y = 11$
$4x - 3y = 1$

11 $x + 2y = 7$
$2x + 3y = 12$

16 $2x - 7y = 17$
$5x + 2y = 23$

12 $7x + 4y = 9$
$3x - 5y = 24$

17 $5x + y = 15$
$3x - 4y = 9$

13 $8x - y = 6$
$7x + 5y = 17$

18 $3x - 4y = 30$
$4x + 5y = 9$

14 $5x + 7y = 4$
$x + 2y = -1$

19 $2x + 3y = 2$
$8x - 9y = 1$

15 $5x - 3y = 11$
$4x + y = 19$

20 $3x - 4y = 7$
$x - 2y = 5$

Solve the following problems by forming pairs of simultaneous equations.

21 The sum of Erica's age and John's age is 31. If Erica is 5 years older than John, find the age of each.

22 Twice a number added to a second number is 23. The first number added to four times the second number is 36. Find the two numbers.

23 At a supermarket five apples and three oranges cost 135 p whereas three apples and five oranges cost 145 p. Find:
(a) the cost of an apple
(b) the cost of an orange
(c) the cost of four apples and seven oranges.

24 At a service station 12 litres of petrol and 1 litre of oil cost £6.80 while 7 litres of petrol and 3 litres of oil cost £5.90. Find:
(a) the cost of 1 litre of petrol
(b) the cost of 18 litres of petrol and 2 litres of oil.

25 A book is sold either as a hardback or as a paperback. Three copies of the hardback and ten copies of the paperback cost £80.40, whereas five copies of the hardback and 21 copies of the paperback cost £156.75. Find the cost of each type of book.

In questions 26 to 30, solve the pairs of equations graphically. In each case draw axes for x and g in the ranges indicated. Take 2 cm as 1 unit on each axis.

26 $x + y = 3$ $-2 \leqslant x \leqslant 4$
$y = 3x - 2$ $-3 \leqslant y \leqslant 4$

27 $x + y = 4$ $0 \leqslant x \leqslant 6$
$3x - 2y = 6$ $-4 \leqslant y \leqslant 3$

28 $y = x + 1$ $-3 \leqslant x \leqslant 3$
$2x + y = 2$ $-2 \leqslant y \leqslant 4$

29 $3x + y = 4$ $0 \leqslant x \leqslant 3$
$y = x - 2$ $-3 \leqslant y \leqslant 5$

30 $x = 3y - 2$ $-3 \leqslant x \leqslant 1$
$y = 3x + 2$ $-1 \leqslant x \leqslant 4$

Exercise 82 Ratio and Proportion

2 = 5,6

1 Give the following ratios in their simplest form:

(a) $5:15$

(b) $24:8$

(c) $21:49$

(d) $8\,cm:12\,cm$

(e) $24\,kg:40\,kg$

(f) $108\,m:84\,m$

(g) $8:16:24$

(h) $9:15:24$

(i) $36:45:18$

2 Write down the larger ratio from each of the following pairs:

(a) $2:3$ or $3:4$

(b) $16:3$ or $12:5$

(c) $2:5$ or $5:12$

(d) $9:4$ or $27:11$

3 Simplify the following ratios:

(a) $50\,p:£2$

(b) $£5:£1.50$

(c) $770\,m:1.4\,km$

(d) $128\,g:2\,kg$

4 Find the missing quantities in the following ratios:

(a) $3:4 = 6:$

(b) $:5 = 6:15$

(c) $\frac{6}{} = \frac{12}{4}$

(d) $15:10 = \quad:4$

(e) $9: \quad = 3:8$

(f) $\frac{24}{16} = \frac{15}{}$

5 (a) Divide £49 into two parts in the ratio $4:3$.

(b) Divide 72 km into two parts in the ratio $3:5$.

(c) Divide 260 g into two parts in the ratio $5:8$.

(d) Divide 78 CDs between two sisters in the ratio $7:6$.

(e) Divide £108 into three parts in the ratio $1:3:5$.

6 Sybil is 8 years old and Dan is 12 years old. Divide £100 between them in the ratio of their ages.

7 The angles of a triangle are in the ratio $4:5:9$. Find the sizes of the three angles.

8 In a school with 1200 pupils, 624 are boys. What is the ratio of the number of boys to the number of girls?

9 The ratio of the number of British cars to foreign cars in a carpark is $5:4$. There are 265 British cars. How many cars are there altogether?

10 Find the map ratio, in the form $1:n$, of a map if:

(a) 10 cm on the map represents 1 km

(b) 1 cm on the map represents $\frac{1}{2}$ km

(c) 500 m is represented by $\frac{1}{4}$ cm on the map

(d) 500 km is represented by 2.5 cm on the map.

216

11 The map ratio of a map is 1 : 50 000. The distance on the map between Woodburn and Axe is 9 cm. What is the true distance between these two places?

12 The map ratio of a map is 1 : 200 000. Find the actual length represented by 4.5 cm on the map.

13 The map ratio of a map is 1 : 10 000. The distance between Farmborough and Fishton is 1.5 km. Find the distance on the map between the points representing these places.

14 Joe can buy five pencils for 60 p. How many can he buy at the same rate for £1.08?

15 Scaffolding can be hired at a daily rate. If it costs £248 to hire some scaffolding for 8 days how much will it cost to hire the same scaffolding for 13 days?

16 An 8 kg bag of potatoes costs 56 p. At the same rate, what would a 50 kg bag cost?

17 The rates of currency exchange displayed in a bank showed that £10 could be exchanged for 96 French francs. How many francs would I get for £35? How many pounds would my cousin get for 528 francs?

18 A school allows 130 exercise books for every 6 pupils. How many exercise books are needed for 27 pupils?

19 Carpet to cover a floor of area 12 m² costs £288. How much would a similar carpet to cover a floor with an area of 17 m² cost?

20 A recipe for Chinese Bean Sprouts to serve four lists the following ingredients:

50 g bacon	20 ml peanut oil
4 spring onions	500 g bean sprouts
root ginger	80 ml chicken stock
4 celery sticks	10 ml soy sauce
100 g mushrooms	

(a) How much will the peanut oil cost if it is sold in litre bottles for £2.50?
(b) Bacon costs £2.80/kg. How much will the bacon required for the recipe cost?
(c) A bottle of soy sauce contains 150 ml. How many servings of Chinese Bean Sprouts should this be sufficient for?
(d) List the ingredients needed to serve ten.

Exercise 83 Pythagoras' ══AT 4 ═ 7
Theorem

1 Find the square of each of the following numbers, giving your answers correct to four significant figures where necessary:

(a) 5.9   (c) 1.4   (e) 3.6   (g) 0.036
(b) 13.6   (d) 0.9   (f) 0.36   (h) 36

2 Find the square roots of each of the following numbers, giving your answers correct to four significant figures:

(a) 8   (c) 31.7   (e) 0.82   (g) 0.0082
(b) 17   (d) 3.17   (f) 0.082   (h) 820

3 In this question give each answer correct to three significant figures.

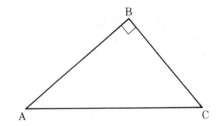

(a) If AB $=$ 7 cm and BC $=$ 5 cm, find AC.
(b) If AB $=$ 8.5 cm and BC $=$ 4.9 cm, find AC.
(c) If AB $=$ 12.4 cm and BC $=$ 8.7 cm, find AC.
(d) If AC $=$ 8.2 cm and BC $=$ 4.9 cm, find AB.
(e) If AC $=$ 24.5 cm and AB $=$ 15.3 cm, find BC.
(f) If BC $=$ 52 cm and AC $=$ 77 cm, find AB.

4 Use Pythagoras' theorem to determine whether the largest angle in each of the triangles with sides of the given lengths, is acute, 90° or obtuse:

(a) 8 cm, 10 cm, and 12 cm
(b) 4.9 cm, 7.3 cm and 9.8 cm
(c) 2.7 cm, 3.6 cm and 4.5 cm
(d) 13 m, 15 m and 24 m
(e) 32 mm, 27 mm and 40 mm
(f) 6.3 cm, 6 cm and 8.7 cm.

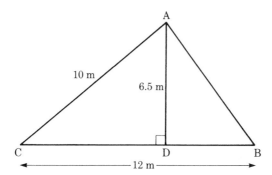

5

A pole 6.5 m high stands on level ground. It is supported in a vertical position by two wires attached to its top and to points on opposite sides of the foot of the pole and 12 m apart. If one wire is 10 m long, find:

(a) the distance from the anchor point of each support wire to the foot of the pole
(b) the length of the other wire.

6 A soccer pitch measures 106 m by 70 m. How far is it between opposite corners?

7 In a rectangle one side is 10 cm and each diagonal is 26 cm. Find its perimeter.

8

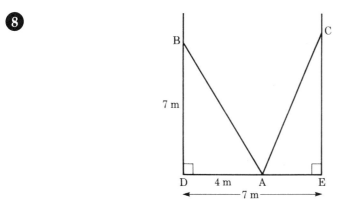

The diagram shows a ladder AB resting on horizontal ground DAE in a narrow street 7 m wide. The foot of the ladder A is 4 m from the base of a vertical wall DB and touches the wall at a point 7 m above the ground. How long is the ladder?
The ladder is now turned about A so that it rests against a vertical building on the opposite side of the street at a point C. How high is C above the ground?

9

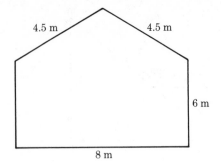

4.5 m   4.5 m

6 m

8 m

The diagram represents the side of a house.

(a) Find the height of the ridge above the ground.
(b) Find the length of a ladder which rests on level ground at a distance 5 m from the base of the side of the house and just reaches the ridge.

10

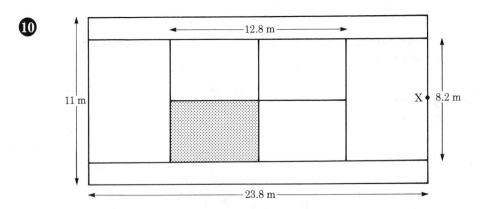

12.8 m

11 m

X   8.2 m

23.8 m

The diagram represents a tennis court. A player standing at X attempts to serve the ball into the shaded rectangle. At the moment of impact the ball is 2.75 m vertically above X. Find the length of the longest direct path that the ball can travel if it is to strike the ground within the shaded area.

11 ABCD is a square of side 4 cm. AX = 3 cm and Y is the midpoint of BC.

(a) Find XD^2, YD^2 and XY^2.
(b) Hence show that $X\hat{Y}D$ is a right angle.

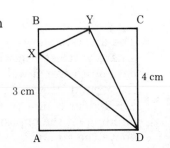

B   Y   C

X

3 cm

4 cm

A   D

Exercise 84 Inequalities ══════AT ③=7,8

Solve the following inequalities, illustrating your solutions on a number line.

1 $x - 3 < 9$

2 $x + 4 < 7$

3 $x - 1 > 4$

4 $x + 5 > -5$

5 $3 < 5 + x$

6 $4 - x > 3$

7 $3 < -x$

8 $5 > 3 - x$

9 $5 - x > -3$

10 $1 - x < -4$

11 $7 \geqslant 2x - 1$

12 $5 - 3x \leqslant 11$

13 $10 - 3x \geqslant 1$

14 $2x - 1 > 2 + x$

15 $3x - 2 \leqslant 2x - 1$

16 $2x \leqslant x - 1$

17 $2x + 1 \geqslant -3$

18 $3x - 2 \geqslant 2x + 1$

19 $2x + 1 > x - 2$

20 $5x + 1 < 4x - 1$

21 Find, where possible, the range of values of x for which both inequalities are valid.

(a) $x > 4$ and $x > 1$
(b) $x > 3$ and $x \leqslant 5$
(c) $x < 1$ and $x > -2$

(d) $x \leqslant 0$ and $x < 2$
(e) $x < -2$ and $x < -4$
(f) $x > -5$ and $x < -3$

22 Solve each of the following pairs of inequalities and then find the range of values of x that satisfy both of them.

(a) $x - 2 < 6$ and $x + 2 > 7$
(b) $x - 1 \leqslant 5$ and $x + 4 \geqslant 2$
(c) $2x + 1 \geqslant 5$ and $3x - 2 < 10$
(d) $2x - 1 > 0$ and $3x - 4 \leqslant 5$

23 Find the range of values of x for which the following inequalities are true:

(a) $x + 4 < 2x + 3 < x + 7$
(b) $2x < x - 2 < 5$
(c) $3x + 1 \geqslant 4x - 1 > 3x - 2$
(d) $x < 4x - 1 < 2x + 1$

Exercise 85 Changing the ══AT═3═ 8
Subject of a Formula

For each formula change the subject to the letter in brackets.

1 $A = P + I$ (I)

2 $D = ST$ (T)

3 $A = lw$ (l)

4 $r = p + q$ (p)

5 $2a = b + c$ (c)

6 $y = mx$ (m)

7 $I = \dfrac{PRT}{100}$ (R)

8 $E = Ri^2$ (R)

9 $v = u + at$ (u)

10 $p = \frac{1}{5}q$ (q)

11 $a = b + 2c$ (c)

12 $z = y - x$ (x)

13 $y = mx + c$ (m)

14 $v = u + at$ (t)

15 $\dfrac{p}{q} = \dfrac{r}{s}$ (s)

16 $A = \frac{1}{2}(a + b)h$ (h)

17 $E = Ri^2$ (i)

18 $A = P + \frac{1}{5}I$ (I)

19 $3c = a - 2b$ (b)

20 $c^2 = a^2 + b^2$ (a)

21 Make a the subject of the formula $v = u + at$.
Find a when $v = 13$, $u = 5$ and $t = 4$.

22 Rearrange the formula $v = \frac{1}{2}u - 5t$ to make u the subject.
Find u when $v = 3$ and $t = 2$.

23 Make c the subject of the formula $s = \frac{1}{2}(a + b + c)$.
Find c when $a = 8$, $b = 5$ and $s = 11$.

24 Rearrange the formula $z = pq + r$ to make p the subject.
Find p if $q = 2$, $r = 10$ and $z = 4$.

25 Make x the subject of the formula $z = \dfrac{24}{x + y}$.
Hence find x when $z = 2$ and $y = 7$.

26 Make s the subject of the formula $v^2 = u^2 + 2as$.
Use this formula to find the value of s when $u = 10$, $v = 20$ and $a = 10$.

27 Make h the subject of the formula $A = \pi r^2 + 2\pi rh$.
Find h when $A = 594$, $\pi = \frac{22}{7}$ and $r = 7$.

28 Make y the subject of the formula $\dfrac{1}{z} = \dfrac{1}{x} + \dfrac{1}{y}$.
Find y when $x = \frac{1}{2}$ and $z = \frac{1}{5}$.

29 Make b the subject of the formula $c = \dfrac{5}{a} + \dfrac{12}{b}$.
Find b when $a = 5$ and $c = 4$.

30 A number z is equal to a number x subtracted from three times a number y.
(a) Find a formula for z in terms of x and y.
(b) Rearrange this formula to give y in terms of x and z.
(c) Find y when $x = 11$ and $z = 10$.

Exercise 86 Removing Brackets

Expand each of the following expressions.

1 (a) $4(a + 5)$ (d) $3(y - 7)$ (g) $5(2a + 1)$
   (b) $2(a - 3)$ (e) $6(3 - a)$ (h) $4(2 - 3b)$
   (c) $5(x + 2)$ (f) $2(1 - x)$ (i) $7(3 - 4x)$

2 (a) $2x(y + 2z)$ (c) $5a(2b + c)$ (e) $3p(q - 2)$
   (b) $3x(2y + 3z)$ (d) $4a(5b - 2c)$ (f) $6x(5y - 2z)$

3 (a) $(a + b)(c + d)$ (c) $(p - q)(r + s)$ (e) $(2a + b)(3c + d)$
   (b) $(a + b)(c - d)$ (d) $(p - q)(r - s)$ (f) $(2p + 3q)(r - 2s)$

4 (a) $(x + 1)(x + 2)$ (d) $(a + 7)(a + 4)$ (g) $(p + 4)(p + 10)$
   (b) $(x + 3)(x + 2)$ (e) $(a + 1)(a + 6)$ (h) $(q + 8)(q + 1)$
   (c) $(x + 5)(x + 4)$ (f) $(b + 3)(b + 5)$ (i) $(r + 6)(r + 7)$

5 (a) $(x - 3)(x - 2)$ (c) $(a - 4)(a - 5)$ (e) $(y - 4)(y - 8)$
   (b) $(x - 5)(x - 6)$ (d) $(p - 9)(p - 3)$ (f) $(z - 1)(z - 10)$

223

6 (a) $(x + 4)(x - 1)$ (c) $(x - 3)(x + 8)$ (e) $(p + 7)(p - 4)$
    (b) $(x - 5)(x + 6)$ (d) $(a + 2)(a + 7)$ (f) $(y - 1)(y + 8)$

7 (a) $(2x + 3)(x + 1)$ (c) $(3x + 2)(x + 5)$ (e) $(4x + 3)(x + 3)$
    (b) $(5x + 2)(x + 2)$ (d) $(x + 3)(2x + 7)$ (f) $(x + 4)(5x + 2)$

8 (a) $(4x - 3)(x + 1)$ (c) $(5a - 7)(a + 4)$ (e) $(7z - 2)(z + 3)$
    (b) $(3x + 2)(x - 1)$ (d) $(b + 3)(3b - 2)$ (f) $(y + 9)(2y - 1)$

9 (a) $(3x + 2)(2x + 5)$ (c) $(7a - 3)(2a + 5)$ (e) $(3a - 2)(3a + 2)$
    (b) $(4x + 1)(3x - 2)$ (d) $(5b + 1)(3b - 2)$ (f) $(4y - 5)(4y + 3)$

10 (a) $(3x + 1)(2 + x)$ (c) $(7x - 2)(3x + 4)$ (e) $(6 + p)(5 - p)$
    (b) $(5a + 3)(1 + 3a)$ (d) $(4 + x)(4 - x)$ (f) $(3x + 5)(3 - x)$

11 (a) $(a + 1)^2$ (c) $(c + 3)^2$ (e) $(x + 5)^2$
    (b) $(b + 2)^2$ (d) $(p + 8)^2$ (f) $(x + 7)^2$

12 (a) $(a + b)^2$ (d) $(3x + 2)^2$ (g) $(2x + y)^2$
    (b) $(p + q)^2$ (e) $(2a + 5)^2$ (h) $(4a + b)^2$
    (c) $(x + y)^2$ (f) $(5b + 7)^2$ (i) $(3a + 5b)^2$

13 (a) $(x - 1)^2$ (d) $(3y - 1)^2$ (g) $(a - 2b)^2$
    (b) $(a - 5)^2$ (e) $(5x - 2)^2$ (h) $(3p - q)^2$
    (c) $(b - 9)^2$ (f) $(4z - 3)^2$ (i) $(2x - 5y)^2$

14 (a) $(x + 3)(x - 3)$ (d) $(3a + 1)(3a - 1)$ (g) $(a + b)(a - b)$
    (b) $(a - 6)(a + 6)$ (e) $(4b - 3)(4b + 3)$ (h) $(p + 3q)(p - 3q)$
    (c) $(b + 5)(b - 5)$ (f) $(7a - 2)(7a + 2)$ (i) $(2a - 3b)(2a + 3b)$

Exercise 87 Algebraic Factors
==AT **3** = $\boxed{7,8}$

Factorise each of the following expressions.

1 (a) $3x + 3$ (c) $6x + 2$ (e) $4x - 12$
    (b) $5a - 5$ (d) $12b + 6$ (f) $5a - 20$

2 (a) $x^2 + 4x$ (d) $5a^2 + a$ (g) $2x^2 + 4x$
    (b) $x^2 - 5x$ (e) $3b - b^2$ (h) $6a^2 - 2a$
    (c) $3x^2 + x$ (f) $3a + 6a^2$ (i) $18y^2 - 6y$

3 (a) $3x^2 + 6x + 9$

(b) $8x^2 - 4x + 16$

(c) $6ab + 2ac - 6ad$

(d) $6xy - 3xz + 9xw$

4 (a) $a + a^3$

(b) $b^3 - b^2$

(c) $2x^2 - 8x^3$

(d) $3y^4 + 9y^2$

5 (a) $ac + ad + bc + bd$

(b) $xy - 2x - 4y + 8$

(c) $pr + ps - qr - qs$

(d) $3pq + 3p - 2q - 2$

(e) $6 - 2b - ab + 3a$

(f) $2a^2 + bc + 2ab + ac$

6 (a) $x^2 + 4x + 3$

(b) $x^2 + 7x + 10$

(c) $x^2 + 9x + 8$

(d) $a^2 + 9a + 20$

(e) $b^2 + 9b + 14$

(f) $y^2 + 6y + 9$

7 (a) $x^2 - 8x + 12$

(b) $x^2 - 9x + 14$

(c) $x^2 - 10x + 21$

(d) $a^2 - 8a + 15$

(e) $b^2 - 9b + 20$

(f) $z^2 - 12z + 32$

8 (a) $x^2 + x - 12$

(b) $x^2 - 5x - 14$

(c) $x^2 + 4x - 21$

(d) $a^2 - 2a - 15$

(e) $b^2 - b - 20$

(f) $z^2 + 4z - 32$

9 (a) $x^2 - 7x - 18$

(b) $x^2 - 11x + 24$

(c) $x^2 + 2x - 35$

(d) $a^2 - 4a - 5$

(e) $b^2 - b - 6$

(f) $z^2 + 11z + 30$

10 (a) $21 + x^2 - 10x$

(b) $9 - 6x + x^2$

(c) $3x - 28 + x^2$

(d) $28 - 11x + x^2$

(e) $3x + x^2 - 10$

(f) $12 - x - x^2$

11 (a) $x^2 - 9$

(b) $a^2 - 4$

(c) $b^2 - 16$

(d) $y^2 - 100$

(e) $x^2 - 49$

(f) $4 - x^2$

(g) $25 - y^2$

(h) $36 - a^2$

(i) $64 - x^2$

12 (a) $2x^2 + 3x + 1$

(b) $2a^2 + a - 3$

(c) $6x^2 + 5x + 1$

(d) $6x^2 + 13x + 6$

(e) $3b^2 + 2b - 8$

(f) $14x^2 + 31x - 10$

(g) $4a^2 + 5ab + b^2$

(h) $10x^2 + 13xy - 3y^2$

13 (a) $4a^2 - 9$

(b) $9x^2 - 16$

(c) $25x^2 - 4$

(d) $4x^2 - 25y^2$

(e) $9a^2 - 4b^2$

(f) $36x^2 - 81y^2$

14 (a) $8a^2 - 4a$

(b) $ac - ad + bc - bd$

(c) $2x^2 - 21 + 11x$

(d) $25a^2 - 1$

(e) $2 - x - 3x^2$

(f) $4a^2 + 4a - 15$

(g) $12x + 5x - 2$

(h) $a^3 + a^2 + a + 1$

225

Exercise 88 Trial and Improvement

1 (a) The equation $4x - x^2 = 1$ has a solution that lies between 3 and 4. Find two numbers, differing by 0.1, each given to one decimal place, between which the solution lies.

(b) The above equation has a second solution between 0.2 and 0.3. Find two numbers, differing by 0.01, each to two decimal places, between which this second solution lies.

For each question from 2 to 7, find two numbers, differing by 0.1, each given to one decimal place, between which a solution to the equation lies.

2 $x^3 - 8x = 2$ (start by trying $x = 3$)

3 $x - \dfrac{15}{x} = 20$ (start by trying $x = 5$)

4 $x - \dfrac{11}{x} = 13$ (start by trying $x = 4$)

5 $x^2 + x - \dfrac{9}{x} = 2$ (start by trying $x = 2$)

6 $x^3 + x^2 - 3x = 2$

7 $x + \dfrac{1}{x^2} = 3$

For each question from 8 to 10, find two numbers differing by 0.01, each given to two decimal places, between which a solution to the given equation lies. Hence write down a solution correct to one decimal place.

8 $x^3 + 2x^2 + 3x = 30$

9 $\dfrac{8}{x} - x^2 = 4$

10 $2x - \dfrac{1}{x^2} = 3$

226

Exercise 89 Probability ====AT 5 = 8
Trees

1 The probability that a given person at a concert is male is $\frac{2}{5}$.
(a) What is the probability that a given person is female?
(b) Two people are chosen at random from the audience. Draw a probability tree and use it to find the probability that:
  (i) both are female
  (ii) one is male and one is female.

2 (a) When a dice is rolled what is the probability of:
  (i) getting a 6   (ii) not getting a 6?
(b) Two dice, one large and one small, are rolled. Find the probability that:
  (i) both dice show 6s
  (ii) exactly one dice shows a 6
  (iii) the sum of the two scores is a perfect square.

3 Box A contains three white discs and four yellow discs, while Box B contains two white discs and three blue discs. A disc is taken at random from the first box, followed by one from the second box. Find the probability that:

(a) both discs are white
(b) exactly one disc is white
(c) the discs are of different colours.

4 Peggy has two five-sided spinners. The possible scores on one are 1, 2, 3, 4 or 5 and the possible scores on the other are 4, 5, 6, 7 or 8. If the two are spun, find the probability that:

(a) the sum of the scores is:
  (i) 5   (ii) 13   (iii) 15   (iv) 10
(b) the product of the two numbers is a prime number
(c) the difference between the two numbers is 4.

5 (a) Two coins are tossed, one after the other. Draw the appropriate probability tree and use it to find the probability that:
  (i) both coins show tails
  (ii) the first shows a head and the second shows a tail
  (iii) at least one shows a tail.
(b) Extend your probability tree to show the various probabilities if three coins are tossed, one after the other. Hence find the probability that:
  (i) all three show heads
  (ii) exactly one shows a tail
  (iii) at least one shows a tail.

6 In a street the probability that a house has a telephone is $\frac{7}{12}$ and the probability that a house has a car is $\frac{3}{4}$.

(a) If there are 108 houses in the street, how many houses:
   (i) have a telephone
   (ii) have a car?
(b) Two houses are chosen at random in the street. What is the probability that:
   (i) both have a car
   (ii) at least one has a telephone?

7 The first of two bags contains two white, three blue and four red marbles, while the second contains four blue and three red marbles. Two marbles are drawn at random, one from each bag.

(a) Draw a probability tree to show this information.
(b) Hence find the probability that:
   (i) two blue marbles are drawn
   (ii) at least one red marble is drawn.

Exercise 90 Quadratic Equations

AT **3** = **7**

Solve the following equations.

1
(a) $x(x - 6) = 0$
(b) $x(x - 5) = 0$
(c) $x(x + 4) = 0$

(b) $(x - 3)x = 0$
(e) $x(x + 8) = 0$
(f) $(x + 3)x = 0$

2
(a) $(x - 2)(x - 4) = 0$
(b) $(x - 3)(x - 9) = 0$
(c) $(x - 5)(x - 1) = 0$
(d) $(x - 4)(x + 5) = 0$

(e) $(x + 1)(x + 8) = 0$
(f) $(x + 7)(x - 5) = 0$
(g) $(x + 3)(x + 11) = 0$
(h) $(x - 6)(x + 2) = 0$

3
(a) $(2x - 3)(x - 1) = 0$
(b) $(3x - 5)(x - 2) = 0$
(c) $x(4x - 1) = 0$
(d) $(2x - 5)(3x - 2) = 0$

(e) $(5x + 1)(2x - 3) = 0$
(f) $(4x - 3)(6x + 5) = 0$
(g) $(3x + 1)(2x + 7) = 0$
(h) $x(7x + 2) = 0$

4
(a) $x^2 - 7x + 10 = 0$
(b) $x^2 - 7x + 12 = 0$
(c) $x^2 - 9x + 8 = 0$

(d) $x^2 - 9x + 18 = 0$
(e) $x^2 - 8x + 15 = 0$
(f) $x^2 - 12x + 35 = 0$

5
(a) $x^2 - 2x - 15 = 0$
(b) $x^2 + 3x - 28 = 0$
(c) $x^2 + 5x - 36 = 0$

(d) $x^2 - 5x - 14 = 0$
(e) $x^2 + 8x - 9 = 0$
(f) $x^2 - 9x - 22 = 0$

6
(a) $x^2 + 8x + 15 = 0$
(b) $x^2 + 16x + 48 = 0$
(c) $x^2 + 7x + 10 = 0$

(d) $x^2 + 13x + 42 = 0$
(e) $x^2 + 16x + 63 = 0$
(f) $x^2 + 16x + 15 = 0$

7
(a) $x^2 = 4$
(b) $x^2 = 9$
(c) $x^2 - 16 = 0$

(d) $x^2 - 36 = 0$
(e) $x^2 - 100 = 0$
(f) $x^2 - 25 = 0$

8
(a) $x^2 - 5x = 0$
(b) $x^2 + 4x = 0$
(c) $4x^2 - x = 0$

(d) $x + 7x = 0$
(e) $3x^2 + 5x = 0$
(f) $5x^2 - 3x = 0$

9
(a) $x^2 - 8x + 16 = 0$
(b) $x^2 - 6x + 9 = 0$
(c) $x^2 - 14x + 49 = 0$

(d) $x^2 + 2x + 1 = 0$
(e) $x^2 + 10x + 25 = 0$
(f) $x^2 - 12x + 36 = 0$

10
(a) $2x^2 - 7x + 3 = 0$
(b) $2x^2 - 11x + 12 = 0$
(c) $3x^2 - 7x + 2 = 0$

(d) $5x^2 + 9x - 2 = 0$
(e) $3x^2 + 10x - 8 = 0$
(f) $4x^2 + 27x - 7 = 0$

11
(a) $12x^2 - 11x + 2 = 0$
(b) $6x^2 - 13x + 6 = 0$
(c) $10x^2 + 3x - 1 = 0$

(d) $8x^2 + 10x - 3 = 0$
(e) $15x^2 + 13x - 2 = 0$
(f) $30x^2 - 23x + 3 = 0$

12
(a) $4x^2 = 1$
(b) $9x^2 = 25$
(c) $16x^2 - 1 = 0$

(d) $9x^2 - 16 = 0$
(e) $25x^2 - 81 = 0$
(f) $100x^2 - 49 = 0$

13
(a) $x^2 - x = 20$
(b) $x^2 + 5x = 14$
(c) $x^2 + 7x = 18$

(d) $x^2 = x + 12$
(e) $6x^2 = x + 2$
(f) $5x^2 = 9x + 2$

14
(a) $x^2 - 16x + 55 = 0$
(b) $x^2 + 10x + 21 = 0$
(c) $2x^2 - 7x = 0$
(d) $9x^2 = 6x + 35$

(e) $9x^2 - 4 = 0$
(f) $x^2 - 12x + 32 = 0$
(g) $x^2 + 6x = 27$
(h) $8x^2 - 14x - 15 = 0$

15 When twice a number x is subtracted from the square of the same number, the answer is 15. Form an equation in x and solve it.

16 Josie thinks of a number x. If she adds twice this number to the square of it the answer is 63. Find the number Josie thinks of.

229

17 Phil is x years old. His father's age is 2 years more than the square of Phil's age and the sum of their ages is 32 years. Form an equation in x and solve it to find the age of each.

18 A rectangle is 3 cm longer than it is wide. If it is x cm wide and its area is 88 cm², form an equation in x and solve it to find the dimensions of the rectangle.

19 One of the parallel sides of a trapezium is 8 cm longer than the other. If the distance between the parallel sides, x cm, is equal to the length of the shorter of the parallel sides and the area of the trapezium is 45 cm², form an equation in x and solve it to find the dimensions of the trapezium.

20 The base of an isosceles triangle is x cm long and its perpendicular height is two-thirds the length of its base. If the area of the triangle is 48 cm², form an equation in x and solve it. What is the height of the triangle and how long is one of the equal sides?

Exercise 91 Recognising ═══AT**3**═ **8** Types of Graphs

In questions 1 to 4 several possible answers are given. Write down the letter that corresponds to the correct answer.

1 The graph of $y = (x - 1)(x + 4)$ could be:

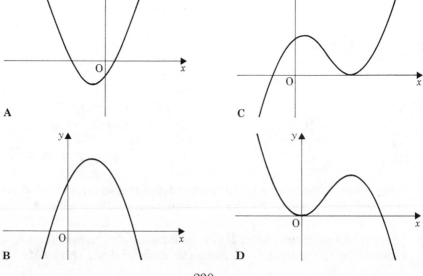

A

C

B

D

230

❷ The graph of $y = x^2 - 4x + 3$ could be:

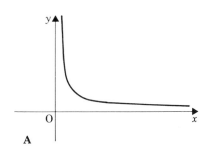

A

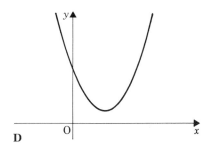

C

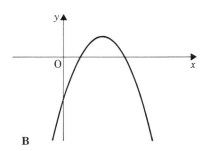

B

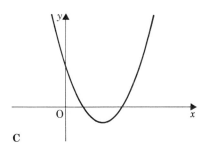

D

❸ The graph of $y = x(x^2 - 4)$ could be:

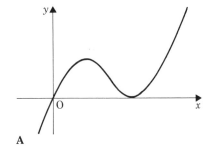

A

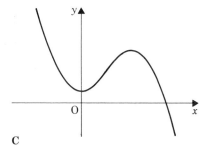

C

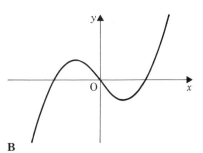

B

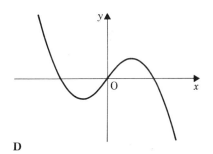

D

4 The graph of $y = \dfrac{12}{x}$ could be:

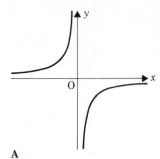

A

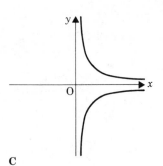

C

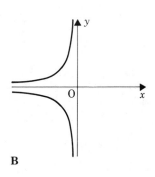

B

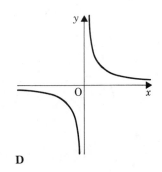

D

5

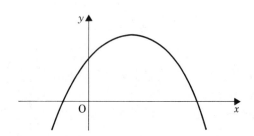

The equation of the graph above could be:

A $y = (x - 2)(x - 5)$ **C** $y = (x - 2)(x - 5)$
B $y = (x + 2)(x + 5)$ **D** $y = (x + 2)(x - 5)$

6 Draw a sketch of the curve given by:

(a) $y = (x - 2)(x - 5)$ (e) $y = x(x - 3)(x - 6)$

(b) $y = (x + 5)(x - 3)$ (f) $y = \dfrac{20}{x}$

(c) $y = (x + 2)(x + 7)$ (g) $y = \dfrac{-12}{x}$

(d) $y = 4 - x^2$ (h) $y = x^2(4 - x)$

Exercise 92 Loci

1 Describe the locus of a point on this page that moves so that it is always 4 cm from the right-hand edge of this page.

2 A is a fixed point. Describe the locus of points that are always 10 cm from A.

3

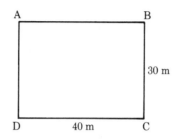

ABCD represents a rectangular flower bed measuring 40 m by 30 m.

(a) Describe the locus of points within the bed that are:
    (i) 20 m from both AD and BC
    (ii) equidistant from B and C
    (iii) equidistant from AB and BC.

(b) Illustrate the locus of points in the bed that are within 25 m of both D and C.

4

A strut, AB, 20 cm long, pivots about a point C, three-quarters of the way along it.

(a) Describe the locus of:
    (i) the point A   (ii) the point B.

(b) In one complete turn about C, how many times further will A travel than B?

5 P is the midpoint of a chord AB in a circle centre O. Describe the locus of P if:

(a) AB moves so that it is always parallel to its original position.

(b) AB moves around the circle but remains constant in length.

6 A farmhouse A, and a water supply, B, are 100 m apart. The farmer wishes to fence off every point that is within 50 m of the water supply and more than 70 m from the house. Illustrate this on a diagram.

7

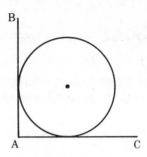

Describe the locus of the centres of circles that touch two straight lines AB and AC that are at right angles (as shown in the diagram above).

8

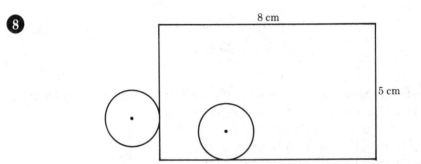

The diagram shows a small rectangular silver box measuring 8 cm by 5 cm.

(a) Describe the locus of the centre of a coin, of diameter 2 cm, that is placed on the base of the box and is rolled so that its edge is always in contact with the side of the box.

(b) Repeat part (a) if the coin is rolled round the outside of the box.

9

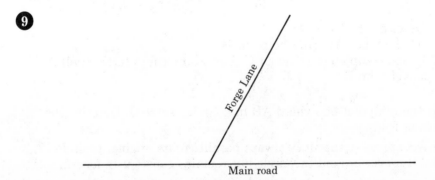

A television mast is to be erected 200 m from a main road and 100 m from Forge Lane. Show on a sketch the possible positions for the mast.

10 (a) AB is a fixed line 8 cm long. Illustrate the locus of a point P such that $A\hat{P}B = 90°$.

   (b) Repeat part (a) if $A\hat{P}B = 60°$.

   (c) Repeat part (a) if $A\hat{P}B = 120°$.

11

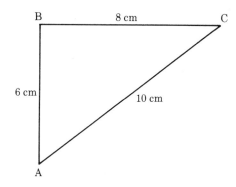

12 A set square is rotated about one of its vertices A. Describe the locus of:

   (a) the vertex B
   (b) the vertex C
   (c) the mid-point of AC.

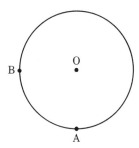

The diagram above shows a circular flowerbed, centre O, with a diameter of 20 m. A and B are points on the circumference such that $A\hat{O}B = 90°$. A gardener is instructed to plant African marigolds in the region of the bed that is within 10 m of both A and B. Illustrate this region on a sketch.

13

A •   B •

A and B represent two trees 40 m apart. Sketch the loci required to show the area that is both nearer to A than to B and is within 30 m of B.

235

Exercise 93 Three-dimensional Problems

1

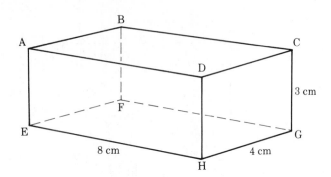

The diagram shows a cuboid. Each face is a rectangle.

(a) How many faces are there?

(b) Which edges are equal in length to CG?

(c) Use Pythagoras' Theorem to find the length of:
   (i) CH   (ii) ED   (iii) EG   (iv) EC.

(d) Use trigonometry to find the size of each of the angles:
   (i) $H\hat{C}G$ (ii) $E\hat{G}H$ (iii) $D\hat{E}H$ (iv) $C\hat{E}G$.

2

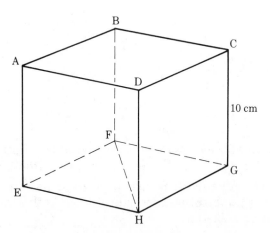

The diagram shows a cubical box. The length of each edge is 10 cm.

(a) How many vertices (corners) does this box have?

(b) How many edges are there? What is the total length of all the edges?

(c) Find the length of the diagonal EC.

236

3

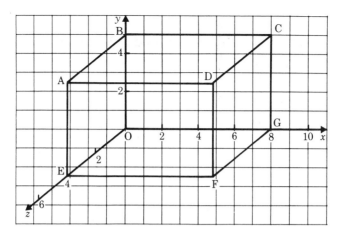

The diagram shows a cuboid with one vertex at the origin. The Ox, Oy and Oz axes lie along three of its edges. Each axis is graduated in units. Find:

(a) the coordinates of all eight vertices
(b) the coordinates of the mid-points of the edges:
    (i) EF   (ii) AE   (iii) DF
(c) the coordinates of the point of intersection of the diagonals AC and BD
(d) the length of:
    (i) EC   (ii) BF.

4

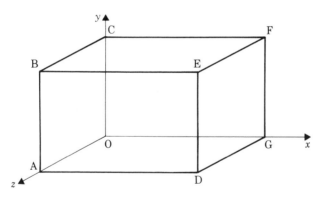

The diagram shows a cuboid with one vertex at O and three of its edges lying along the axes.

(a) If E is the point (4, 3, 12), write down the coordinates of each of the other vertices.
(b) Find the length of:
    (i) OD   (ii) CG   (iii) AF.

5 A cuboid is to have edges of lengths 2 units, 3 units and 4 units. One of the vertices is to be placed at the point (2, 3, 4) and every edge must lie along or be parallel to one of the axes. How many different positions of the cuboid are possible?

Exercise 94 Trigonometry ═══AT**4**═ 8

1 For each of the following diagrams write down (as a fraction and as a decimal correct to four decimal places) the sine, cosine and tangent of the marked angle.

(a)

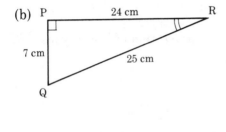

(c)

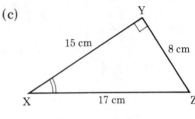

(b)

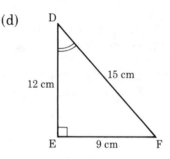

(d)

2 Find: (i) the sine   (ii) the cosine   (iii) the tangent, of each of the following angles. Give your answers correct to four decimal places.

(a) 37°
(b) 54.8°
(c) 8.2°
(d) 127°
(e) 78.5°

3 Find:

(a) the acute angle with a sine of:
   (i) 0.3742   (ii) 0.8261

(b) the acute angle with a cosine of:
   (i) 0.4493   (ii) 0.7125

(c) the acute angle with a tangent of:
   (i) 0.6235   (ii) 1.4926.

In questions 4 to 9, use the information given in the diagram to find $\hat{A}$.

4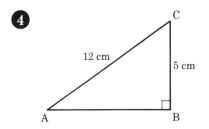

7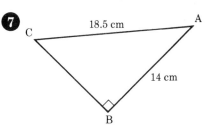

5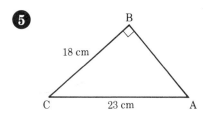

8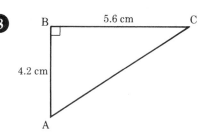

6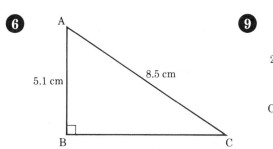

9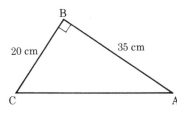

In questions 10 to 15, use the information given in the diagram to find the required length.

10 Find AC.

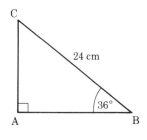

11 Find QR.

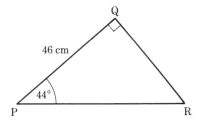

12 Find YZ.

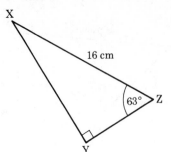

14 Find DE.

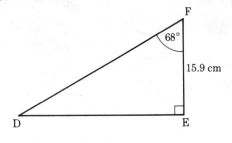

13 Find LN.

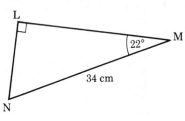

15 Find HJ.

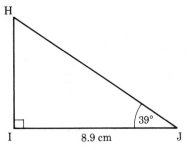

16 In triangle PQR, $\hat{Q} = 90°$, PQ = 15 cm and PR = 22 cm. Find $\hat{R}$.

17 In triangle LMN, $\hat{L} = 90°$, MN = 17 cm and ML = 6 cm. Find $\hat{M}$.

18 In triangle XYZ, $\hat{Y} = 90°$, XY = 3.8 cm and YZ = 5.4 cm. Find $\hat{X}$.

19 The angle of elevation of the top of a building from a point on level ground 450 m away is 18°. Find the height of the building.

20

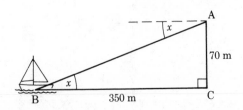

A boat B is 350 m from the foot C of a vertical cliff that is 70 m high. What is the angle of depression of the boat from the top of the cliff?

240

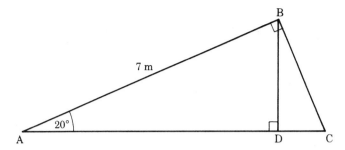

21

The diagram represents a roof truss. Find:

(a) the height of the ridge B above the horizontal AC
(b) the length of the shorter sloping side, BC
(c) the span of the truss AC.

22 From the top of a building that is 40 m high, the angles of depression of the near side and far side of a road that runs parallel to the building are 29.2° and 25.8°. How wide is the road?

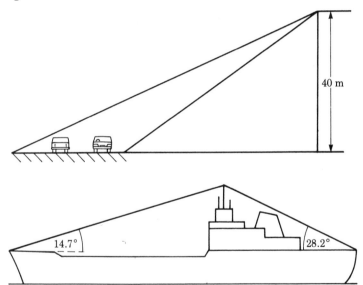

23

The angles of elevation of the top of the bridge of a ship from the bow and the stern are respectively 14.7° and 28.2°. If the top of the bridge is 18.5 m above the level of the deck find the length of the deck.

24 A man walks 55 m away from the base of a vertical building and finds that the elevation of the top of the building is 32.4°. How high is the building? He continues to walk away from the building in the same straight line until he reaches another point, from which the elevation of the top is 26.7°. How far has he walked from the foot of the building?

Exercise 95 Statistics 3 ═══AT 5 = 7,8

1 This table shows the distribution of the marks obtained by third-year pupils sitting a geography test.

Mark	0–9	10–19	20–29	30–39	40–49
Frequency	3	5	26	35	16

(a) Find:
   (i) the modal group   (ii) the group that contains the median.
(b) Estimate the likely mean score.
(c) Draw a histogram for this data and superimpose a frequency polygon.

2 The table shows the distribution of goals scored by the twenty-eight teams in a football league.

Number of goals scored	35–39	40–44	45–49	50–54	55–59	60–64	65–69	70–74
Frequency	1	2	8	5	6	3	0	3

(a) Find:
   (i) the modal group   (ii) the group that contains the median.
(b) Estimate the mean number of goals scored.
(c) Estimate the range.
(d) Draw a histogram and superimpose a frequency polygon.

3 The following frequency table was made from information about the heights (in cm) of a group of children.

Height (h cm)	$120 \leqslant h < 125$	$125 \leqslant h < 130$	$130 \leqslant h < 135$	$135 \leqslant h < 140$
Frequency	3	5	9	12

Height (h cm)	$140 \leqslant h < 145$	$145 \leqslant h < 150$	$150 \leqslant h < 155$
Frequency	6	4	1

(a) Draw, on separate diagrams:
   (i) a histogram
   (ii) a frequency polygon,
   to represent the data given in the table.
(b) Estimate:
   (i) the range   (ii) the median.
(c) Draw the cumulative frequency curve for this data and use it to estimate:
   (i) the median
   (ii) the upper and lower quartiles
   (iii) the interquartile range.

242

4 This table shows the heights after ten weeks of the plants grown from a single packet of seeds.

Height of plant (h cm)	$0 \leqslant h < 5$	$5 \leqslant h < 10$	$10 \leqslant h < 15$
Frequency	7	15	24

Height of plant (h cm)	$15 \leqslant h < 20$	$20 \leqslant h < 25$	$25 \leqslant h < 30$
Frequency	38	18	3

Draw a cumulative frequency curve for this data and use it to find

(a) the median
(b) the upper and lower quartiles
(c) the interquartile range.